My Book

This book belongs to

Name: ______________________________

©All rights reserved-Math-Knots LLC., VA-USA

Copy right © 2019 MATH-KNOTS LLC

All rights reserved, no part of this publication may be reproduced, stored in any system or transmitted in any form, or by any means, electronic, mechanical, photocopying, recording, or otherwise without the written permission of MATH-KNOTS LLC.

Cover Design by :
Gowri Vemuri

First Edition :
January, 2019

Second Edition :

April, 2021

Author :
Gowri Vemuri

Edited by :
Ritvik Pothapragada

Questions: mathknots.help@gmail.com

Dedication

This book is dedicated to:

My Mom, who is my best critic, guide and supporter.

To what I am today, and what I am going to become tomorrow,

is all because of your blessings, unconditional affection and support.

This book is dedicated to the

strongest women of my life ,

my dearest mom

and

to all those moms in this universe.

G.V.

©All rights reserved-Math-Knots LLC., VA-USA

Visit www.a4ace.com

Also available more time based practice tests on subscription

©All rights reserved-Math-Knots LLC., VA-USA

What is SCAT ?

School and College Ability Test (SCAT)

John Hopkins University, Center for Talent Search **(CTY)** offers enriched/advance programs during academic year and summer for children from grade 2-12. To get enrolled into these programs, **CTY conducts a screening test (SCAT), which is designed above grade level to challenge the kids.** Student scores are compared to the other students at the same and above grade level.

Based on child's test scores, CTY recommends advanced courses that they offer during academic year and summer. High scoring students are also recognized at a CTY awards ceremony.

SCAT Test Format

The SCAT test comprises of Verbal and Quantitative sections, each section has 55 questions.

Verbal Section measures a student's understanding of the meaning of words and relationship between them. Multiple-choice Questions are given. Students are required to identify the analogy between pair of words and complete the analogy from the given choices.

Quantitative Section measures mathematical reasoning ability of students. Students are required to compare the quantities and determine, whether two values are equal, or one is greater or lesser over the other. They all need to identify if the information provided is sufficient to solve the problem.

SCAT test categories :

Grades	Test Level (Grades)	Verbal Scoring Range	Quantitative Scoring Range	Test Timing/Breaks
2-3	4-5	401-471	412-475	Each section 22 mins with 10 min break
4-5	6-8	405-482	419-506	Each section 22 mins with 10 min break
6 and above	9-12	410-494	424-514	Each section 22 mins with 10 min break

©All rights reserved-Math-Knots LLC., VA-USA

What is SCAT ?

Scoring Process:

Score will be based on the number of questions the student answers correctly out of the 50 scored questions in each section. Scores are compared against higher grade score. For example, Grade 2 students are compared to a general population of 4th graders, Grade 3 to Grade 5, Grade 4 to Grade 6, Grade 5 to Grade 8, Grade 6 to Grade 9, Grade 7 to Grade 12 and Grade 8 to Grade 12.

Student Grade	Test Level (Grades)	Scores compared Grade	Minimum scores for Qualification (Verbal)	Minimum scores for Qualification (Quantitative)
2	4-5	4	>=430	>=435
3	4-5	5	>=435	>=440
4	6-8	6	>=440	>=450
5	6-8	8	>=445	>=465
6	9-12	9	>=450	>=470
7	9-12	12	>=455	>=475
8	9-12	12	>=460	>=480

INTERPRETING YOUR CHILD'S TEST RESULTS:

Level and Form: There are different difficulty levels and forms of the SCAT. Difficulty levels are tied to a student's grade in school. Research has shown that grades are more closely related to academic performance than students' age. The "Level and Form" code is a record of exactly which test your child took on the indicated test date.

Raw Score: The raw score is the number of questions your child answered correctly out of 50. On each of the two subtests, there are 50 items that count toward the total raw score.

Scaled Score: CTY uses the scaled score to compare the performance of students taking various forms of the test and to determine eligibility for programs and awards. Scaled scores range from 400 to 514 depending on the subtest and level of the test.

©All rights reserved-Math-Knots LLC., VA-USA

What is SCAT ?

Percentile: The percentile shows how your child's results compare to a sample of students from the general population that are in a higher, comparison grade. For example, a 7th grade test-taker in the 63rd percentile compared to grade 12 means the 7th grader scored

better than or equal to 63 percent of a sample of 12th graders. More specifically, it is estimated

that this student may be able to reason better than or equal to 63 percent of 12th graders but

not that they know more than or equal to 63 percent of 12th graders.

©All rights reserved-Math-Knots LLC., VA-USA

What is SCAT ?

TEST TAKING TIPS:

These are general tips for taking the SCAT :

- Make sure you eat and drink well before the test. Hungry and thirsty brains can't think well.
- Have few scratch papers and pencils ready though it is a computer-based test it will be helpful.
- Remember you are taking above grade level test.
- Time is the essence of finishing the test.
- If you are spending much time on a question move on.
- If you can't answer a question, move on and not worry much. If possible, make a note on the scratch paper so that you can revisit the question at the end. You can come back later to answer time permitting by pressing the PREVIOUS button.
- For the questions you want to recheck If possible, make a note on the scratch paper so that you can revisit the question at the end. You can come back later to answer time permitting by pressing the PREVIOUS button.
- Read the question and all multiple choices before answering.
- There is no penalty for wrong answers, so guessing is OK.
- Remember: Rechecking is resolving the problem again.
- Finally, be confident, and good luck!

PREPARATION FOR THE TEST

1. Student needs to have few blank papers, pencils and eraser to do their work.
2. Student need to read the questions carefully and think through the multiple choices.
3. Student need to make sure they are selecting the answers correctly.

Before the testing date.

1. Make sure the child has a good nights sleep and a good breakfast.

©All rights reserved-Math-Knots LLC., VA-USA

INSTRUCTIONS:

Each question comprises of two parts,

First part is marked as (I).

Second part is marked as (I I).

Compare the two parts and choose the correct answer from the given choices.

©All rights reserved-Math-Knots LLC., VA-USA

©All rights reserved-Math-Knots LLC., VA-USA

www.a4ace.com www.math-knots.com

Sample

(I) 1 + 0
(II) 0 + 8

(A) I is greater than II

(B) I is less than II

(C) I is equal to II

(D) None of these

Sample Solution

(I) 1 + 0 = 1
(II) 0 + 8 = 8

One is less than eight. Option B is the right Choice to Choose.

©All rights reserved-Math-Knots LLC., VA-USA

©All rights reserved-Math-Knots LLC., VA-USA

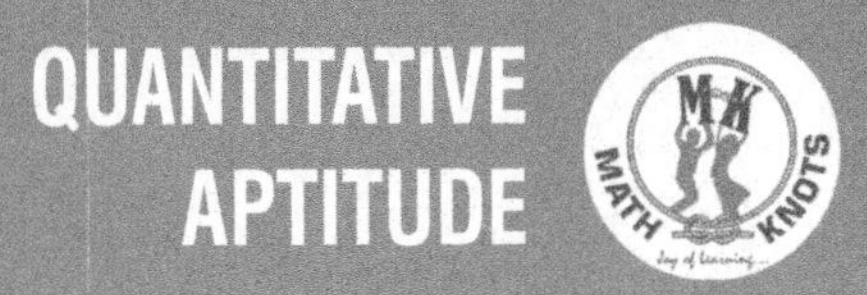

1.

(I) Find a number which when divided by 48 gives quotient 20 and remainder 21.

(II) 981

(A) I is greater than II (B) I is less than II

(C) I is equal to II (D) None of these

2.

(I) Find the value of (15625 ÷ 25) ÷ 5

(II) 120

(A) I is greater than II (B) I is less than II

(C) I is equal to II (D) None of these

3. (I) 1016

(II) The population of a city is 56,840. If one out of every 56 people is working in police, how many police personnel are there in the town?

(A) I is greater than II (B) I is less than II

(C) I is equal to II (D) None of these

4. (I) 0 ÷ 345

(II) 1

(A) I is greater than II (B) I is less than II

(C) I is equal to II (D) None of these

©All rights reserved-Math-Knots LLC., VA-USA

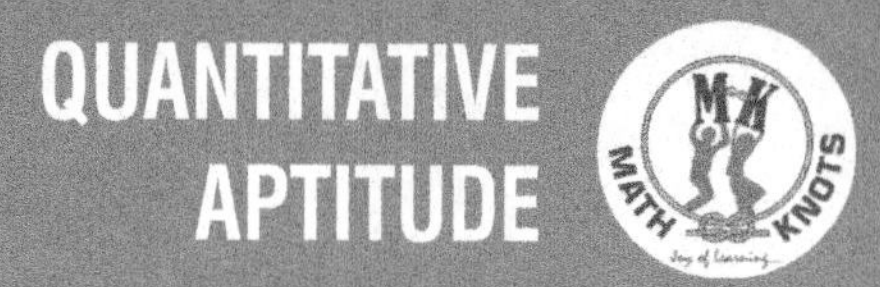

5.

(I) **Any non-zero whole number divided by itself**

(II) **1**

(A) I is greater than II (B) I is less than II

(C) I is equal to II (D) None of these

6.

(I) **Length of side of a square whose area is 169 $inches^2$.**
(II) **23 inches**

(A) I is greater than II (B) I is less than II

(C) I is equal to II (D) None of these

7.

(I) **Length = 12.5 feet**
(II) **Length of a rectangle whose area is 225 ft^2 and width is 9 ft.**

(A) I is greater than II (B) I is less than II

(C) I is equal to II (D) None of these

8.

(I) **Area of a square whose side measures 1.5 inches?**
(II) **2.225 square inches**

(A) I is greater than II (B) I is less than II

(C) I is equal to II (D) None of these

©All rights reserved-Math-Knots LLC., VA-USA

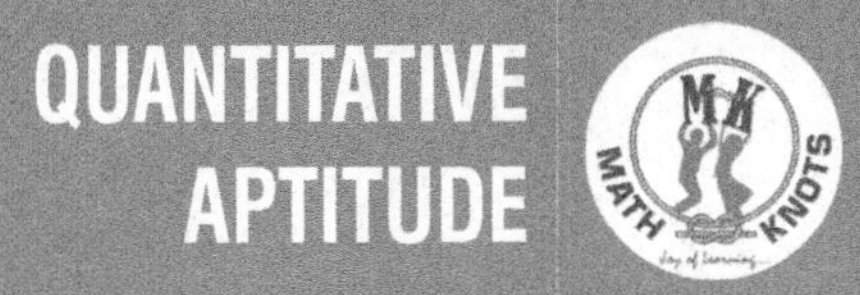

9.

(I) **Find the area of a rectangular park whose length is 56 yards and width is 25 yards.**

(II) **14000 yard^2**

(A) I is greater than II (B) I is less than II

(C) I is equal to II (D) None of these

10.

(I) **Angles of an isosceles right triangle.**

(II) **Angles are 45^0, 45^0 and 90^0**

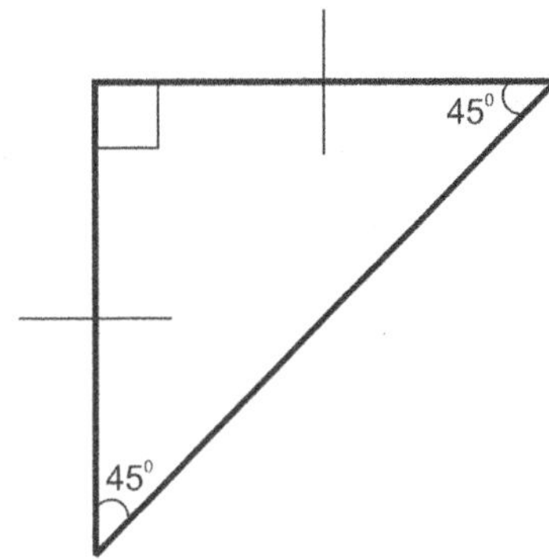

(A) I is greater than II (B) I is less than II

(C) I is equal to II (D) None of these

11.

(I) **2a - 5 = 3**

(II) **a = 3**

(A) I is greater than II (B) I is less than II

(C) I is equal to II (D) None of these

©All rights reserved-Math-Knots LLC., VA-USA

12.

(I) $5x - 8 = 2x - 1$

(II) $x = 2$

(A) I is greater than II

(B) I is less than II

(C) I is equal to II

(D) None of these

13.

(I) $(-6) - (+6)$

(II) $(-5) - (+6)$

(A) I is greater than II

(B) I is less than II

(C) I is equal to II

(D) None of these

14.

(I) $34 \times 34 \times 34 \times 34 \times 34$

(II) $(34)^5$

(A) I is greater than II

(B) I is less than II

(C) I is equal to II

(D) None of these

15.

(I) $(-63)^8$

(II) $(-63) \times (-63) \times (-63) \times (-63) \times (-63) \times (-63) \times (-63)$

(A) I is greater than II

(B) I is less than II

(C) I is equal to II

(D) None of these

©All rights reserved-Math-Knots LLC., VA-USA

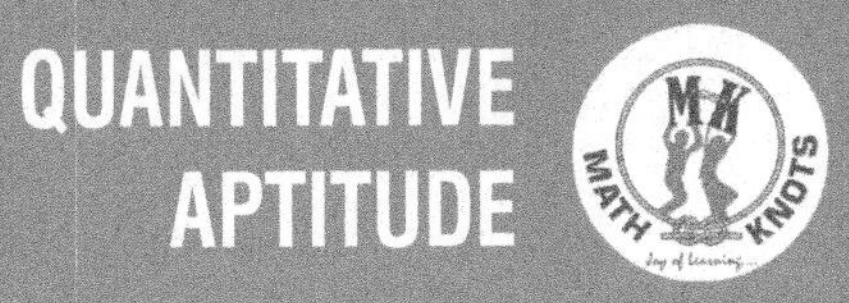

16.

(I) 2^4
(II) 4^2

(A) I is greater than II
(B) I is less than II
(C) I is equal to II
(D) None of these

17.

(I) $(11)^3 \times (11)^4 \times (11)^{11}$
(II) $(11)^{18}$

(A) I is greater than II
(B) I is less than II
(C) I is equal to II
(D) None of these

18.

(I) $1,000,000 \div (-100)$
(II) $-1,000$

(A) I is greater than II
(B) I is less than II
(C) I is equal to II
(D) None of these

19.

(I) $(-84) \div$ ____ $= -3$
(II) 38

(A) I is greater than II
(B) I is less than II
(C) I is equal to II
(D) None of these

©All rights reserved-Math-Knots LLC., VA-USA

20.

(I) Divide 0 by -341
(II) 1

(A) I is greater than II
(B) I is less than II
(C) I is equal to II
(D) None of these

21.

(I) Divide (-135) by (-15)
(II) -8

(A) I is greater than II
(B) I is less than II
(C) I is equal to II
(D) None of these

22.

(I) 72 ÷ (-9).
(II) -9

(A) I is greater than II
(B) I is less than II
(C) I is equal to II
(D) None of these

23.

(I) (2826) ÷ (-2)
(II) -1403

(A) I is greater than II
(B) I is less than II
(C) I is equal to II
(D) None of these

©All rights reserved-Math-Knots LLC., VA-USA

24.

(I) $(+912) \div (-19)$

(II) -48

(A) I is greater than II

(B) I is less than II

(C) I is equal to II

(D) None of these

25.

(I) Simplify: $(-2) \times [1 - 3 + 6 \div (-2)] + 4$

(II) 24

(A) I is greater than II

(B) I is less than II

(C) I is equal to II

(D) None of these

26.

(I) $345 + 5640 \div 10$

(II) 909

(A) I is greater than II

(B) I is less than II

(C) I is equal to II

(D) None of these

27.

(I) Simplify: $2 - [3 - \{1 - (2 - 3) + 4 - 3 \text{ of } (1 - 2)\}]$

(II) 6

(A) I is greater than II

(B) I is less than II

(C) I is equal to II

(D) None of these

©All rights reserved-Math-Knots LLC., VA-USA

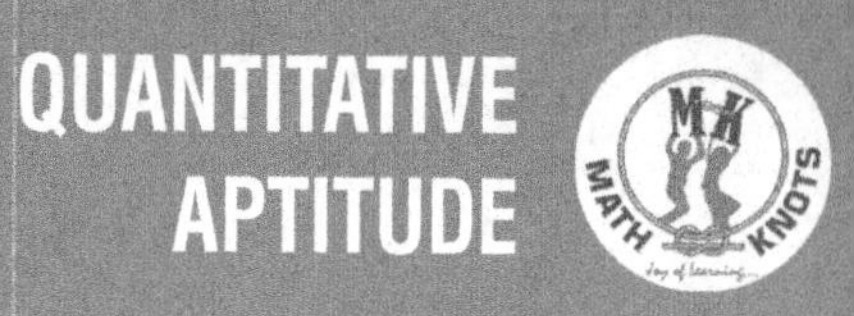

28.

(I) Simplify: (-4) + [(2 - 3) + (5 - 3)]
(II) -5

(A) I is greater than II
(B) I is less than II
(C) I is equal to II
(D) None of these

29.

(I) Simplify: (-1) + [5 - {1 - (7 - 3)}]
(II) 7

(A) I is greater than II
(B) I is less than II
(C) I is equal to II
(D) None of these

30.

(I) [1 - 3 + {(-4) - 5} - 2]
(II) -11

(A) I is greater than II
(B) I is less than II
(C) I is equal to II
(D) None of these

31.

(I) (-25) + 5 ÷ (10 - 5)
(II) -24

(A) I is greater than II
(B) I is less than II
(C) I is equal to II
(D) None of these

©All rights reserved-Math-Knots LLC., VA-USA

32.

(I) 40 - {30 - 20 - [7 (6 - (2 + 3))]}

(II) 36

(A) I is greater than II

(B) I is less than II

(C) I is equal to II

(D) None of these

33.

(I) Prime factorization of 5125

(II) 5 X 5 X 41

(A) I is greater than II

(B) I is less than II

(C) I is equal to II

(D) None of these

34.

(I) Prime factorization of 4000

(II) 2 X 2 X 2 X 2 X 2 X 5 X 5 X 5

(A) I is greater than II

(B) I is less than II

(C) I is equal to II

(D) None of these

35.

(I) Prime factorization of 625

(II) 5 X 5 X 5

(A) I is greater than II

(B) I is less than II

(C) I is equal to II

(D) None of these

©All rights reserved-Math-Knots LLC., VA-USA

36.

(I) Prime factorization of 450.

(II) 2 X 3 X 3 X 3 X 5 X 5

(A) I is greater than II
(B) I is less than II
(C) I is equal to II
(D) None of these

37.

(I) Prime factorization of 864

(II) 2^5 X 3^3

(A) I is greater than II
(B) I is less than II
(C) I is equal to II
(D) None of these

38.

(I) Prime factorization of 252

(II) 2 X 2 X 3 X 3 X 7

(A) I is greater than II
(B) I is less than II
(C) I is equal to II
(D) None of these

39.

(I) Sum of the angles of a Triangle

(II) Sum of the angles of a Rectangle

(A) I is greater than II
(B) I is less than II
(C) I is equal to II
(D) None of these

©All rights reserved-Math-Knots LLC., VA-USA

40.

(I) The product of the HCF and LCM of 6 and 12

(II) 72

(A) I is greater than II

(B) I is less than II

(C) I is equal to II

(D) None of these

41.

(I) LCM of 54, 60 and 72

(II) 1006

(A) I is greater than II

(B) I is less than II

(C) I is equal to II

(D) None of these

42.

(I) The HCF of two numbers is 30 and their product is 5400. Find their LCM.

(II) 108

(A) I is greater than II

(B) I is less than II

(C) I is equal to II

(D) None of these

43.

(I) Largest number that divides 26 and 30 leaving a remainder 2.

(II) 3

(A) I is greater than II

(B) I is less than II

(C) I is equal to II

(D) None of these

©All rights reserved-Math-Knots LLC., VA-USA

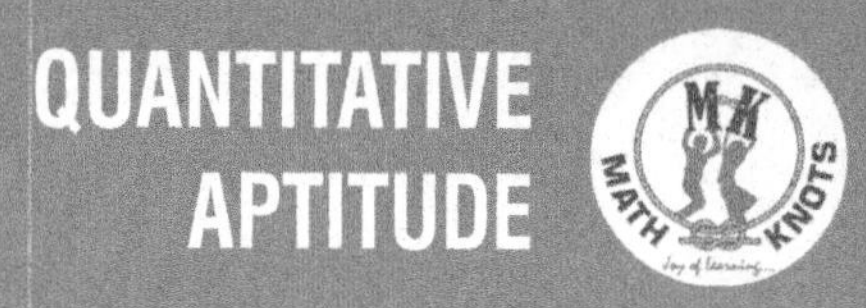

44.

(I) **HCF (Highest common factor) of : 154,140**
(II) **24**

(A) I is greater than II (B) I is less than II

(C) I is equal to II (D) None of these

45.

(I) **HCF of 300, 350 and 100**
(II) **50**

(A) I is greater than II (B) I is less than II

(C) I is equal to II (D) None of these

46.

(I) **Common factors of 4, 12 and 16**
(II) **1, 2 and 3.**

(A) I is greater than II (B) I is less than II

(C) I is equal to II (D) None of these

47.

(I) **The smallest multiple of 16**
(II) **32**

(A) I is greater than II (B) I is less than II

(C) I is equal to II (D) None of these

©All rights reserved-Math-Knots LLC., VA-USA

48.

(I) **The greatest factor of any number**

(II) **The number itself**

(A) I is greater than II

(B) I is less than II

(C) I is equal to II

(D) None of these

49.

(I)

(II) **Obtuse Angle**

(A) I is greater than II

(B) I is less than II

(C) I is equal to II

(D) None of these

50.

(I) **Supplementary angles**

(II) **80° + 50°**

(A) I is greater than II

(B) I is less than II

(C) I is equal to II

(D) None of these

©All rights reserved-Math-Knots LLC., VA-USA

51.

(I) Supplementary angles

(II) $90° + 90°$

(A) I is greater than II (B) I is less than II

(C) I is equal to II (D) None of these

52.

(I) Complementary angles

(II) $45° + 45°$

(A) I is greater than II (B) I is less than II

(C) I is equal to II (D) None of these

53.

(I) Subtract $(x^2 + 2x - 3)$ from $(10 - 3x)$.

(II) $(13 - 5x - x^2)$

(A) I is greater than II (B) I is less than II

(C) I is equal to II (D) None of these

54.

(I) 8 less than 21 decreased by a

(II) $(21 - a) - 8$

(A) I is greater than II (B) I is less than II

(C) I is equal to II (D) None of these

©All rights reserved-Math-Knots LLC., VA-USA

55.

(I) **Coefficient of x in $(4x + 3y^2)$.**
(II) **3**

(A) I is greater than II
(B) I is less than II
(C) I is equal to II
(D) None of these

56.

(I) **3 more than x. (where x is a whole number)**
(II) **$x - 3$**

(A) I is greater than II
(B) I is less than II
(C) I is equal to II
(D) None of these

57.

(I) **Twice the sum of x and y**
(II) **$2 (x + y)$.**

(A) I is greater than II
(B) I is less than II
(C) I is equal to II
(D) None of these

58.

(I) **If $p = 2$ and $q = -3$, find the value of $p^2 - q^2$**
(II) **-4**

(A) I is greater than II
(B) I is less than II
(C) I is equal to II
(D) None of these

©All rights reserved-Math-Knots LLC., VA-USA

59.

(I) If x = 3/5 and y = -5/7, find the value $(x/y)^2$

(II) $(21/25)^2$

(A) I is greater than II (B) I is less than II

(C) I is equal to II (D) None of these

60.

(I) If x = 1, y = 2, z = 0 find the value of $(x + y)^2 + z^2$

(II) 5

(A) I is greater than II (B) I is less than II

(C) I is equal to II (D) None of these

61.

(I) Range of the data : 2.4, 3.1, 2.8, 2.0, 2.7, 3.3, 2.6

(II) 1.5

(A) I is greater than II (B) I is less than II

(C) I is equal to II (D) None of these

62.

(I) $\frac{(5^{-2})^3}{5^3}$

(II) 5^{-9}

(A) I is greater than II (B) I is less than II

(C) I is equal to II (D) None of these

©All rights reserved-Math-Knots LLC., VA-USA

63.

(I) $9^{(-5/2 + 3/2 - 1/2)}$

(II) 9^{-3}

(A) I is greater than II (B) I is less than II

(C) I is equal to II (D) None of these

64.

(I) $\sqrt{225}$

(II) 15

(A) I is greater than II (B) I is less than II

(C) I is equal to II (D) None of these

65.

(I) Find the smallest number with which 147 must be multiplied to get a perfect square.

(II) 2

(A) I is greater than II (B) I is less than II

(C) I is equal to II (D) None of these

66.

(I) $(2^3)^{-2}$

(II) 2^6

(A) I is greater than II (B) I is less than II

(C) I is equal to II (D) None of these

©All rights reserved-Math-Knots LLC., VA-USA

67.

(I) Find the value of x, if $5^x \times 3^x = 50625$

(II) 8

(A) I is greater than II (B) I is less than II

(C) I is equal to II (D) None of these

68.

(I) $(9)^3 \times (9)^{-6}$

(II) $(9)^{-3}$

(A) I is greater than II (B) I is less than II

(C) I is equal to II (D) None of these

69.

(I) Simplify: $(3^3)^{-2}$

(II) 3

(A) I is greater than II (B) I is less than II

(C) I is equal to II (D) None of these

70.

(I) ABCD is a rhombus with $\angle DCB = 38°$. Find $\angle CBD$.

(II) 92

(A) I is greater than II (B) I is less than II

(C) I is equal to II (D) None of these

©All rights reserved-Math-Knots LLC., VA-USA

71.

(I) ABCD is a rectangle with $\angle BAC = 22°$. Determine $\angle DBC$.

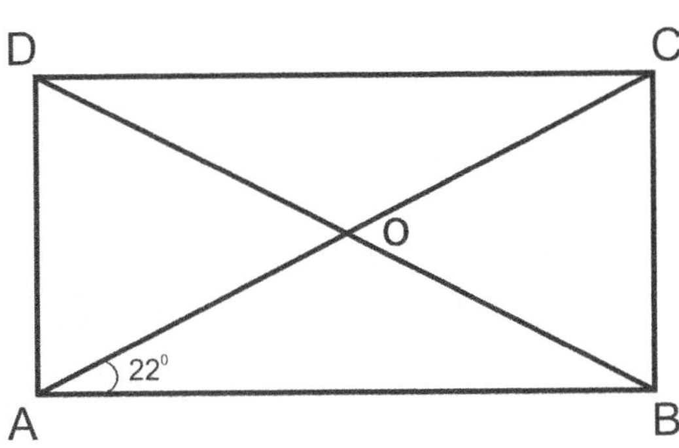

(II) $\angle DBC = 22°$

(A) I is greater than II (B) I is less than II

(C) I is equal to II (D) None of these

72.

(I) O is the center of the given circle. If $\angle XYZ = 80°$, find the measure of $\angle XOZ$.

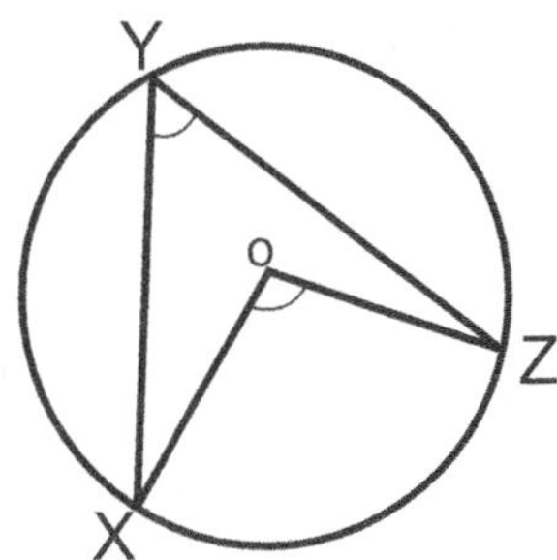

(II) $\angle XOZ = 160°$

(A) I is greater than II (B) I is less than II

(C) I is equal to II (D) None of these

©All rights reserved-Math-Knots LLC., VA-USA

73.

(I) PQRS is a cyclic quadrilateral. If $\angle S = 82°$ and $\angle P = 98°$, find $\angle Q$.

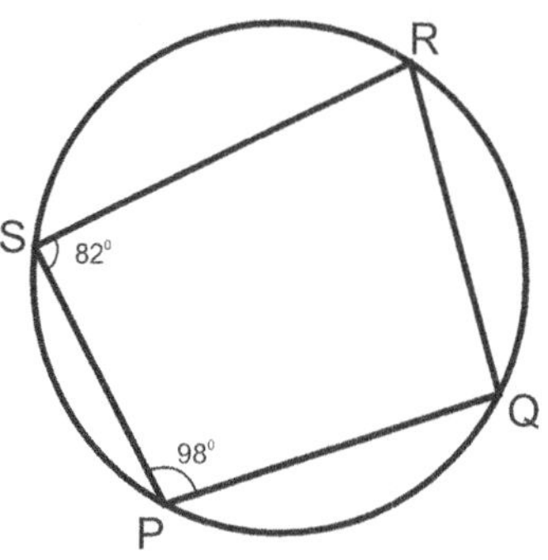

(II) $\angle Q = 82°$

(A) I is greater than II

(B) I is less than II

(C) I is equal to II

(D) None of these

74.

(I) A field is in the form of a triangle with area 3 hectare. If the length of its base is 200 meters, find its altitude.

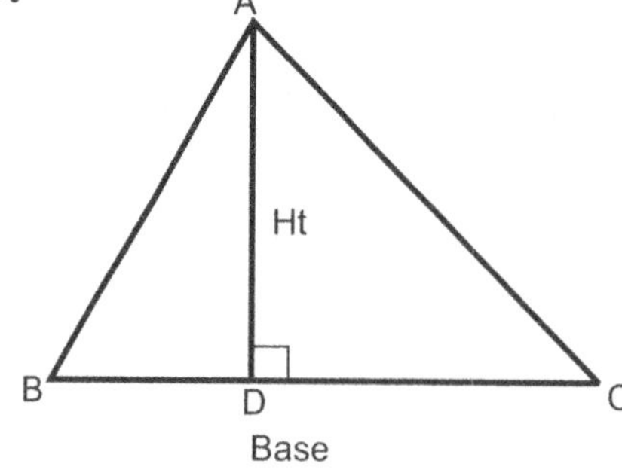

(II) 3000 meters

(A) I is greater than II

(B) I is less than II

(C) I is equal to II

(D) None of these

©All rights reserved-Math-Knots LLC., VA-USA

75.

(I) The parallel sides of a trapezium are 10 inches and 15 inches in length. The distance between these sides is 8 inches. Find the area of the trapezium.

(II) Area = 100 $inches^2$

(A) I is greater than II (B) I is less than II

(C) I is equal to II (D) None of these

76.

(I) The area of a trapezium is 351 ft^2. If the parallel sides of the trapezium measure 17 ft and 22 ft respectively, find the height of the trapezium.

(II) Height = 17 ft.

(A) I is greater than II (B) I is less than II

(C) I is equal to II (D) None of these

77.

(I) Height = 15 inches

(II) The area of rhombus is 119 $inches^2$ and its perimeter is 56 inches. Find its altitude.

(A) I is greater than II (B) I is less than II

(C) I is equal to II (D) None of these

©All rights reserved-Math-Knots LLC., VA-USA

78.

(I) **Area of a rhombus whose diagonals measure 15 inches and 21 inches.**

(II) **Area = 157.5 inches^2**

(A) I is greater than II (B) I is less than II

(C) I is equal to II (D) None of these

79.

(I) **The radius of a circle whose area is 2,464 ft^2**

(II) **Radius = 28 ft.**

(A) I is greater than II (B) I is less than II

(C) I is equal to II (D) None of these

80.

(I) **The circumference of a circle whose radius is 21 inches. (Take, Π = 22/7)**

(II) **Circumference of a circle = 136 inches**

(A) I is greater than II (B) I is less than II

(C) I is equal to II (D) None of these

81.

(I) **The area of a circle whose diameter is 8.4 inches. (Consider, π = 22/7)**

(II) **Area = 55.44 inches^2**

(A) I is greater than II (B) I is less than II

(C) I is equal to II (D) None of these

©All rights reserved-Math-Knots LLC., VA-USA

82.

(I) $\sqrt[3]{(-729/4913)}$.

(II) (9/17)

(A) I is greater than II

(B) I is less than II

(C) I is equal to II

(D) None of these

83.

(I) **In the figure given below, AB || CD and MN is a transversal line. Find the unknown angle.**

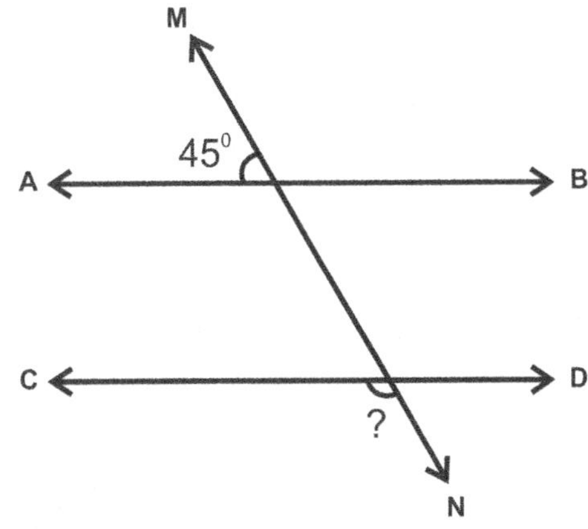

(II) $\angle 135°$.

(A) I is greater than II

(B) I is less than II

(C) I is equal to II

(D) None of these

84.

(I) **Between 12 PM to 5.10 PM hours hand has turned through an angle**

(II) $\angle 155°$

(A) I is greater than II

(B) I is less than II

(C) I is equal to II

(D) None of these

©All rights reserved-Math-Knots LLC., VA-USA

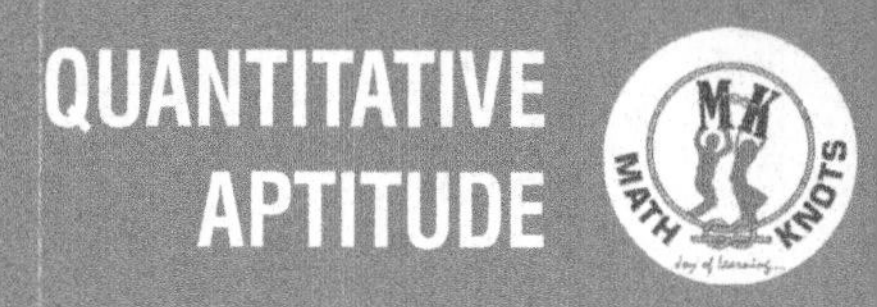

85.

(I) **How many times does the hands of a clock make right angle in a day ?**

(II) **22**

(A) I is greater than II (B) I is less than II

(C) I is equal to II (D) None of these

86.

(I) **Letters of the word APPLE can be arranged in how many ways ?**

(II) **60**

(A) I is greater than II (B) I is less than II

(C) I is equal to II (D) None of these

87.

(I) **Probability of getting a number greater than 4, when a dice is rolled**

(II) **1/4**

(A) I is greater than II (B) I is less than II

(C) I is equal to II (D) None of these

©All rights reserved-Math-Knots LLC., VA-USA

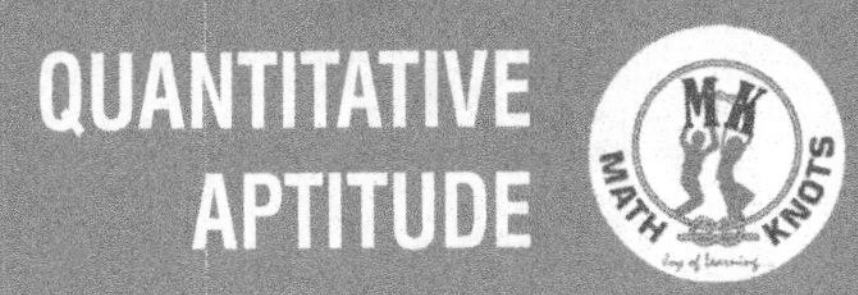

88.

(I) Volume of the box with dimensions 0.8 inches X 0.6 inches X 2.5 inches

(II) 4.50 Cubic inches

(A) I is greater than II

(B) I is less than II

(C) I is equal to II

(D) None of these

89.

(I) Find | x - y |, when x = (- 5) and y = (-11/5)

(II) (-14/5)

(A) I is greater than II

(B) I is less than II

(C) I is equal to II

(D) None of these

90.

(I) $\left|\frac{-9}{7} + \frac{-11}{13}\right|$

(II) $\frac{104}{21}$

(A) I is greater than II

(B) I is less than II

(C) I is equal to II

(D) None of these

91.

(I) $\left(\frac{-1}{8}\right)^{(-1)}$

(II) 8

(A) I is greater than II

(B) I is less than II

(C) I is equal to II

(D) None of these

©All rights reserved-Math-Knots LLC., VA-USA

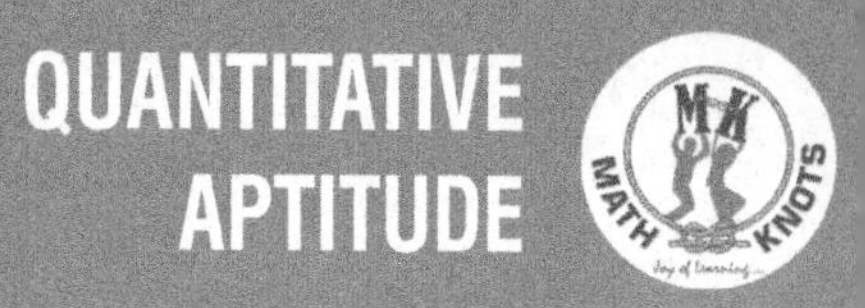

92.

(I) $\left(\frac{3}{-5}\right)^{(3)}$

(II) $\frac{-27}{125}$

(A) I is greater than II
(B) I is less than II
(C) I is equal to II
(D) None of these

93.

(I) **Express $\frac{-81}{256}$ in exponential form.**

(II) $\left(\frac{3}{4}\right)^{(4)}$

(A) I is greater than II
(B) I is less than II
(C) I is equal to II
(D) None of these

94.

(I) **Earth's circumference is 4×10^4 km. What is its circumference in meters?**

(II) **40,000,00 meters.**

(A) I is greater than II
(B) I is less than II
(C) I is equal to II
(D) None of these

95.

(I) **11.2×10^{-6}**

(II) **0.000112**

(A) I is greater than II
(B) I is less than II
(C) I is equal to II
(D) None of these

©All rights reserved-Math-Knots LLC., VA-USA

96.

(I) GCF of 12 and 54
(II) 3

(A) I is greater than II
(B) I is less than II
(C) I is equal to II
(D) None of these

97.

(I) 11
(II) GCF of 66 and 22

(A) I is greater than II
(B) I is less than II
(C) I is equal to II
(D) None of these

98.

(I) 66.01 X 2.22
(II) (66 + 0.01) X (2 + 0.22)

(A) I is greater than II
(B) I is less than II
(C) I is equal to II
(D) None of these

99.

(I) Least common Multiple of 3 and 7
(II) ∏ X 7

(A) I is greater than II
(B) I is less than II
(C) I is equal to II
(D) None of these

©All rights reserved-Math-Knots LLC., VA-USA

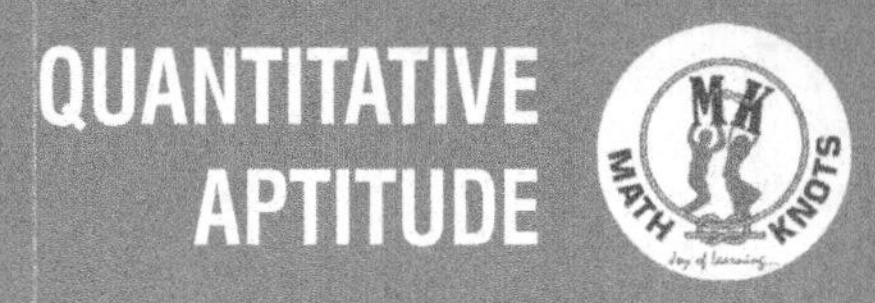

100.

(I) **Area of a Circle X 1/2**

(II) **∏ X Length of radius X Length of radius**

(A) I is greater than II (B) I is less than II

(C) I is equal to II (D) None of these

101.

(I) **5^5**

(II) **625**

(A) I is greater than II (B) I is less than II

(C) I is equal to II (D) None of these

102.

(I) **Least Common Multiple (LCM) of 6 and 9**

(II) **9 X 2**

(A) I is greater than II (B) I is less than II

(C) I is equal to II (D) None of these

103.

(I) **55 meters below sea level**

(II) **55 meters**

(A) I is greater than II (B) I is less than II

(C) I is equal to II (D) None of these

©All rights reserved-Math-Knots LLC., VA-USA

104.

(I) **9° below zero**
(II) **-9°**

(A) I is greater than II
(B) I is less than II
(C) I is equal to II
(D) None of these

105.

(I) **19° below freezing point**
(II) **-18^0**

(A) I is greater than II
(B) I is less than II
(C) I is equal to II
(D) None of these

106.

(I) **88 %**
(II) **0.80**

(A) I is greater than II
(B) I is less than II
(C) I is equal to II
(D) None of these

107.

(I) **Debt of one thousand dollars and 9 cents**
(II) **1000.09**

(A) I is greater than II
(B) I is less than II
(C) I is equal to II
(D) None of these

©All rights reserved-Math-Knots LLC., VA-USA

108.

(I) Elevation of 5505.25 feet above sea level
(II) -5505.25

(A) I is greater than II
(B) I is less than II
(C) I is equal to II
(D) None of these

109.

(I) Gain of $55.45
(II) - 55.40

(A) I is greater than II
(B) I is less than II
(C) I is equal to II
(D) None of these

110.

(I) Area of the Circle / Perimeter of the Circle
(II) Radius / 2

(A) I is greater than II
(B) I is less than II
(C) I is equal to II
(D) None of these

111.

(I) Loss of $3333
(II) $3333

(A) I is greater than II
(B) I is less than II
(C) I is equal to II
(D) None of these

©All rights reserved-Math-Knots LLC., VA-USA

112.

(I) Loss of $9842.99
(II) -$9842.99

(A) I is greater than II
(B) I is less than II
(C) I is equal to II
(D) None of these

113.

(I) Gain of $1,000,050
(II) $1,000,000

(A) I is greater than II
(B) I is less than II
(C) I is equal to II
(D) None of these

114.

(I) Reciprocal of 2/3
(II) 3/2

(A) I is greater than II
(B) I is less than II
(C) I is equal to II
(D) None of these

115

(I) | -0.89 |
(II) - 0.88

(A) I is greater than II
(B) I is less than II
(C) I is equal to II
(D) None of these

©All rights reserved-Math-Knots LLC., VA-USA

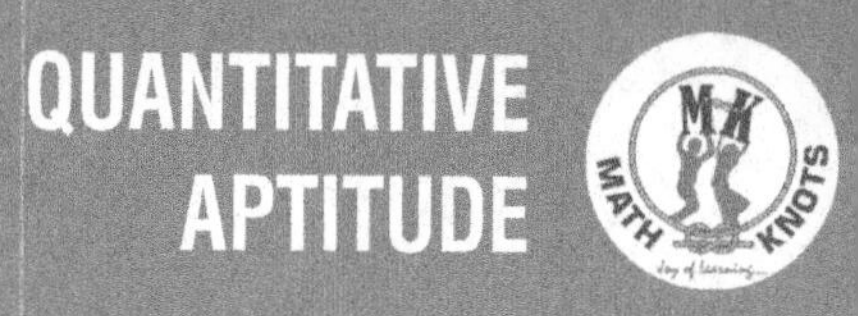

116.

(I) Opposite of 999
(II) -999

(A) I is greater than II
(B) I is less than II
(C) I is equal to II
(D) None of these

117.

(I) Additive Identity
(II) 1

(A) I is greater than II
(B) I is less than II
(C) I is equal to II
(D) None of these

118.

(I) Multiplicative Identity
(II) 1

(A) I is greater than II
(B) I is less than II
(C) I is equal to II
(D) None of these

119.

(I) $(7a + 11) + (9a - 4)$
(II) $16a + 7$

(A) I is greater than II
(B) I is less than II
(C) I is equal to II
(D) None of these

©All rights reserved-Math-Knots LLC., VA-USA

120.

(I) $8(a - 3) + 11(a + 14)$

(II) $19a - 24$ (where a is a whole number)

(A) I is greater than II (B) I is less than II

(C) I is equal to II (D) None of these

121.

(I) Area of a triangle with base as 9 units and height as 5 units

(II) 12.5 square units

(A) I is greater than II (B) I is less than II

(C) I is equal to II (D) None of these

122.

(I) Mean of 31, 31, 37, 34,35

(II) 33.6

(A) I is greater than II (B) I is less than II

(C) I is equal to II (D) None of these

123.

(I) Area of a Square with a side length of 11 inches

(II) 120 inches

(A) I is greater than II (B) I is less than II

(C) I is equal to II (D) None of these

©All rights reserved-Math-Knots LLC., VA-USA

124.

(I) Area = 92 square feet

(II) Area of a Square with a side length of 8 feet

(A) I is greater than II (B) I is less than II

(C) I is equal to II (D) None of these

125.

(I) Area of a Rectangle with a side of length of 5 units and 4 units.

(II) 10 X 2 sq.units

(A) I is greater than II (B) I is less than II

(C) I is equal to II (D) None of these

126.

(I) John buys toffees at the rate of 4 for a dollar and sells them at the rate of 3 for a dollar. Find his profit in percent.

(II) 33.303 %

(A) I is greater than II (B) I is less than II

(C) I is equal to II (D) None of these

©All rights reserved-Math-Knots LLC., VA-USA

127.

(I) An electrician sells a room heater for \$342, gaining $\frac{1}{5}$th of its cost price. Find his profit in percent.

(II) 20%

(A) I is greater than II
(B) I is less than II
(C) I is equal to II
(D) None of these

128.

(I) Charles bought a bicycle for \$425 and sold it for \$459. Find the gain percent.

(II) 12%

(A) I is greater than II
(B) I is less than II
(C) I is equal to II
(D) None of these

129.

(I) $25 \div 200$

(II) 0.1

(A) I is greater than II
(B) I is less than II
(C) I is equal to II
(D) None of these

130.

(I) Find the cost price when selling price is \$700 and loss is 20%

(II) \$875

(A) I is greater than II
(B) I is less than II
(C) I is equal to II
(D) None of these

©All rights reserved-Math-Knots LLC., VA-USA

131.

(I) Express 13/16 as a percent
(II) 81.25%

(A) I is greater than II
(B) I is less than II
(C) I is equal to II
(D) None of these

132.

(I) Express 0.32 as a percent.
(II) 320%

(A) I is greater than II
(B) I is less than II
(C) I is equal to II
(D) None of these

133.

(I) Express 24% as a decimal
(II) 0.024

(A) I is greater than II
(B) I is less than II
(C) I is equal to II
(D) None of these

134.

(I) Find x, if 5% of x = 475
(II) 950

(A) I is greater than II
(B) I is less than II
(C) I is equal to II
(D) None of these

©All rights reserved-Math-Knots LLC., VA-USA

135.

(I) **20 yards cloth is required to make 25 shirts. How much cloth is required to make 35 shirts of the same size?**

(II) **29**

(A) I is greater than II (B) I is less than II

(C) I is equal to II (D) None of these

136.

(I) **If 8 ft long iron rod of uniform thickness weighs 28 lb, what will be the weight of 10 ft long iron rod of the same thickness**

(II) **35 lb**

(A) I is greater than II (B) I is less than II

(C) I is equal to II (D) None of these

137.

(I) **Cube root of (- 3375/2197)**

(II) **15/-13**

(A) I is greater than II (B) I is less than II

(C) I is equal to II (D) None of these

©All rights reserved-Math-Knots LLC., VA-USA

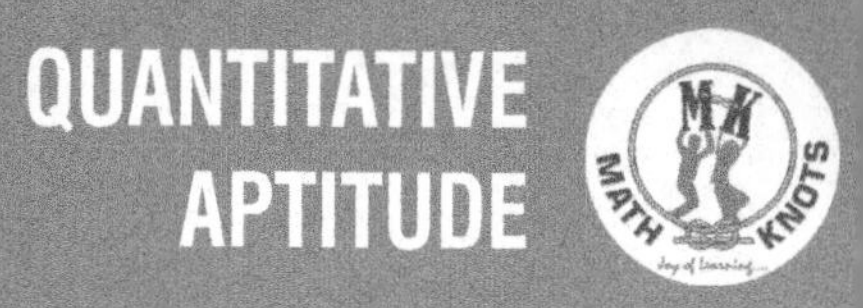

138.

(I) The volume of a cubical box is 166.375 cubic inches. Find the length of each side of the box.

(II) 5.5 inches

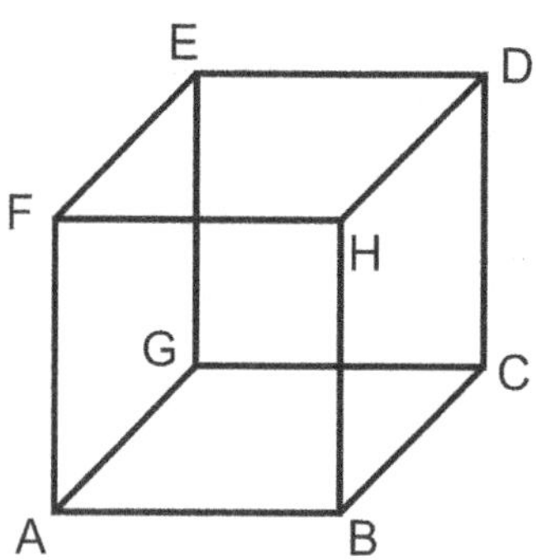

(A) I is greater than II

(B) I is less than II

(C) I is equal to II

(D) None of these

139.

(I) Find the $\sqrt[3]{1331}$

(II) 11

(A) I is greater than II

(B) I is less than II

(C) I is equal to II

(D) None of these

140.

(I) Find the smallest number with which 392 should be multiplied to make it a perfect cube.

(II) 6

(A) I is greater than II

(B) I is less than II

(C) I is equal to II

(D) None of these

©All rights reserved-Math-Knots LLC., VA-USA

141.

(I) 24^4

(II) 12^6

(A) I is greater than II
(B) I is less than II
(C) I is equal to II
(D) None of these

142.

(I) 20^3

(II) 2000

(A) I is greater than II
(B) I is less than II
(C) I is equal to II
(D) None of these

143.

(I) $50^3 \times 20^3$

(II) 10000

(A) I is greater than II
(B) I is less than II
(C) I is equal to II
(D) None of these

144.

(I) Find the smallest number by which 243 should be divided so that the quotient is a perfect cube

(II) 9

(A) I is greater than II
(B) I is less than II
(C) I is equal to II
(D) None of these

©All rights reserved-Math-Knots LLC., VA-USA

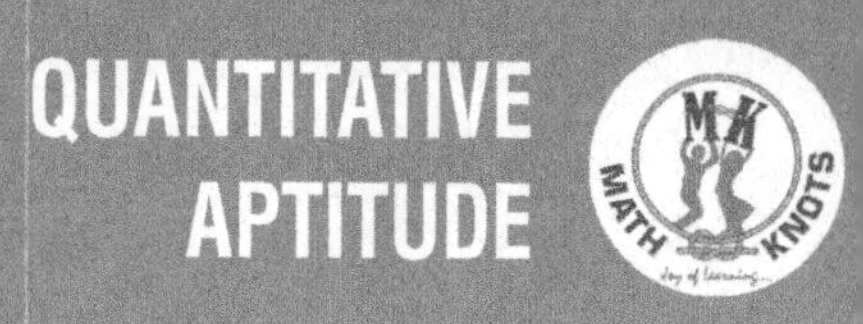

145.

(I) $\sqrt{72} \times \sqrt{450}$

(II) 160

(A) I is greater than II

(B) I is less than II

(C) I is equal to II

(D) None of these

146.

(I) 806.5%

(II) 8.065

(A) I is greater than II

(B) I is less than II

(C) I is equal to II

(D) None of these

147.

(I) $\sqrt{\frac{63504}{65025}}$

(II) $\frac{84}{85}$

(A) I is greater than II

(B) I is less than II

(C) I is equal to II

(D) None of these

148.

(I) $\sqrt{\frac{49}{225} \times \frac{625}{196}}$

(II) $\frac{25}{6}$

(A) I is greater than II

(B) I is less than II

(C) I is equal to II

(D) None of these

©All rights reserved-Math-Knots LLC., VA-USA

149.

(I) Area of the circle / Perimeter of the semi-circle

(II) Radius / 2

(A) I is greater than II

(B) I is less than II

(C) I is equal to II

(D) None of these

150.

(I) Area of the Square / Perimeter of the Square

(II) Side length of the Square / 2

(A) I is greater than II

(B) I is less than II

(C) I is equal to II

(D) None of these

151.

(I) $\sqrt{(81/289)} \times \sqrt{(324/2916)}$

(II) $\frac{3}{13}$

(A) I is greater than II

(B) I is less than II

(C) I is equal to II

(D) None of these

152.

(I) $\sqrt{\frac{121}{169}}$

(II) $\frac{11}{7}$

(A) I is greater than II

(B) I is less than II

(C) I is equal to II

(D) None of these

©All rights reserved-Math-Knots LLC., VA-USA

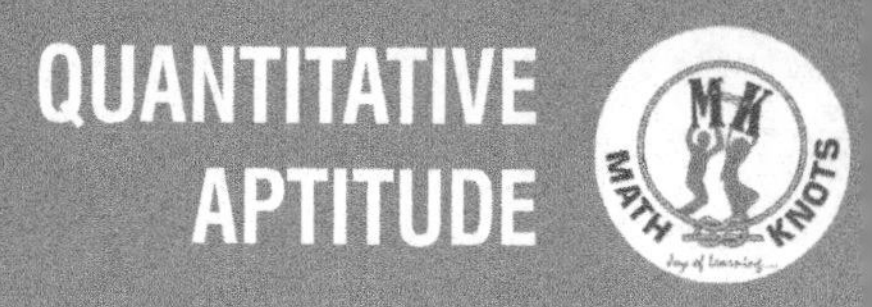

153.

(I) The surface area of a ball is 113.04 inches^2. Find the volume of the ball. (Given, Π= 3.14)

(II) 113 inches^3

(A) I is greater than II (B) I is less than II

(C) I is equal to II (D) None of these

154.

(I) Find the volume of a sphere whose diameter is 24 inches. (Given, Π = 3.14)

(II) 7234.56 inches^3

(A) I is greater than II (B) I is less than II

(C) I is equal to II (D) None of these

155.

(I) The circumference of the base of a right circular cylinder is 62.8 inches and its height is 15 inches. Find the volume of the cylinder. (Given, Π = 3.14)

(II) 4710 inches^3

(A) I is greater than II (B) I is less than II

(C) I is equal to II (D) None of these

156.

(I) $\sqrt{0.0625}$

(II) 0.5

(A) I is greater than II (B) I is less than II

(C) I is equal to II (D) None of these

©All rights reserved-Math-Knots LLC., VA-USA

157.

(I) $\sqrt{1089}$

(II) 33

(A) I is greater than II (B) I is less than II

(C) I is equal to II (D) None of these

158.

(I) Arithmetic mean of first twelve natural numbers.

(II) 6.0

(A) I is greater than II (B) I is less than II

(C) I is equal to II (D) None of these

159.

(I) Mean of first fifteen even numbers.

(II) 15

(A) I is greater than II (B) I is less than II

(C) I is equal to II (D) None of these

160.

(I) Mean of first 10 prime numbers.

(II) 12.5

(A) I is greater than II (B) I is less than II

(C) I is equal to II (D) None of these

©All rights reserved-Math-Knots LLC., VA-USA

161.

(I) The marks obtained by 15 students are as follows:
53, 48, 68, 87, 67, 84, 29, 34, 91, 44, 45, 32, 65, 19, 35. If 35 is the pass mark, how many students have failed?

(II) 1

(A) I is greater than II

(B) I is less than II

(C) I is equal to II

(D) None of these

162.

(I) The points obtained by 10 students are as follows:
53, 48, 87, 67, 34, 91, 45, 32, 19, 35
How many students have scored more than 65 points?

(II) 5

(A) I is greater than II

(B) I is less than II

(C) I is equal to II

(D) None of these

163.

(I) A die was thrown 20 times and the following scores were obtained
1, 5, 3, 4, 2, 6, 2, 5, 3, 1
4, 2, 1, 4, 3, 2, 4, 6, 3, 4
What is the most frequent score

(II) 4

(A) I is greater than II

(B) I is less than II

(C) I is equal to II

(D) None of these

©All rights reserved-Math-Knots LLC., VA-USA

164.

(I) $5 - \frac{2(x-4)}{4} = \frac{(2x+3)}{2}$

(II) $x = 3.7$

(A) I is greater than II
(B) I is less than II
(C) I is equal to II
(D) None of these

165.

(I) $(p + 1) / (p - 3) = 3/ 4$
(II) 13

(A) I is greater than II
(B) I is less than II
(C) I is equal to II
(D) None of these

166.

(I) $(x^2 + 4) / (3x^2 + 7) = \frac{1}{2}$ (where x is positive)
(II) 0.11

(A) I is greater than II
(B) I is less than II
(C) I is equal to II
(D) None of these

167.

(I) $(x^2 + 5) (x^2 - \frac{1}{5})$

(II) $x^4 + \frac{24x^2}{5} - 1$

(A) I is greater than II
(B) I is less than II
(C) I is equal to II
(D) None of these

©All rights reserved-Math-Knots LLC., VA-USA

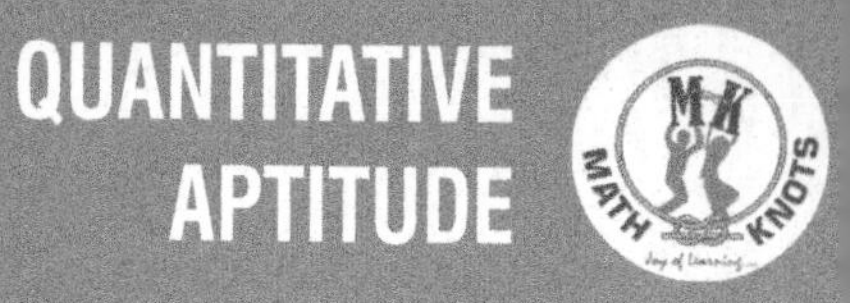

168.

(I) $4(x + 2) - x = 5x + 11$

(II) -2/3 Feet

(A) I is greater than II (B) I is less than II

(C) I is equal to II (D) None of these

169.

(I) After 12 years Sam will be three times as old as he was 4 years ago. Find his present age.

(II) 12

(A) I is greater than II (B) I is less than II

(C) I is equal to II (D) None of these

170.

(I) The sum of two consecutive odd numbers is 92. Find the least nuber.

(II) 47

(A) I is greater than II (B) I is less than II

(C) I is equal to II (D) None of these

©All rights reserved-Math-Knots LLC., VA-USA

171.

(I) The sides of a triangle are in the ratio 3:5:4. If the perimeter of the triangle is 48 inches, find the measure of its greatest side.

(II) 16

(A) I is greater than II
(B) I is less than II
(C) I is equal to II
(D) None of these

172.

(I) The ratio of two numbers is 3:7 and their sum is 100. Find the least of two numbers.

(II) 65

(A) I is greater than II
(B) I is less than II
(C) I is equal to II
(D) None of these

©All rights reserved-Math-Knots LLC., VA-USA

173.

(I) A room 14 ft by 12 ft is to be paved with stones, each measuring 0.25 ft by 0.2 ft. Find the number of stones required to pave the room.

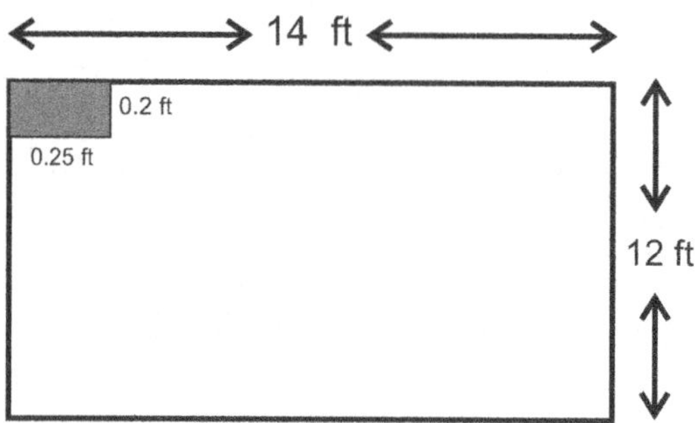

(II) 336

(A) I is greater than II

(B) I is less than II

(C) I is equal to II

(D) None of these

174.

(I) Find the product of 2x and $(3x - 4y^2)$

(II) $6x^2 - 8xy^2$

(A) I is greater than II

(B) I is less than II

(C) I is equal to II

(D) None of these

©All rights reserved-Math-Knots LLC., VA-USA

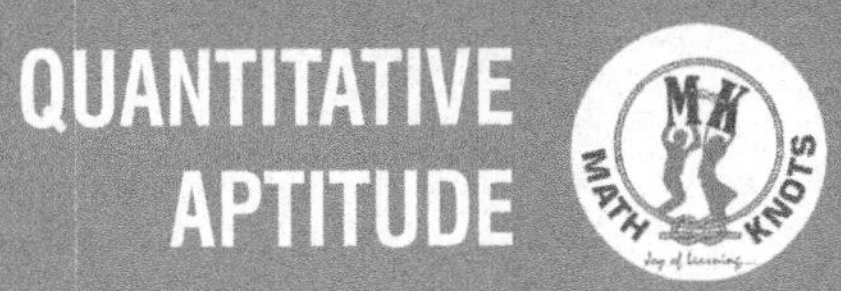

175.

(I) $(2x + 5y)(2x - 5y)$

(II) $4x^2 + 25y^2$

(A) I is greater than II (B) I is less than II

(C) I is equal to II (D) None of these

176.

(I) Area of a Semi Circle X 1/2

(II) ∏ X Length of radius X Length of radius X 1/4

(A) I is greater than II (B) I is less than II

(C) I is equal to II (D) None of these

177.

(I) 27^8

(II) 3^{16}

(A) I is greater than II (B) I is less than II

(C) I is equal to II (D) None of these

178.

(I) Expand the following: $\left(2a + \frac{b}{7}\right)^2$

(II) $4a^2 + \frac{4ab}{7} + \frac{b^2}{49}$

(A) I is greater than II (B) I is less than II

(C) I is equal to II (D) None of these

©All rights reserved-Math-Knots LLC., VA-USA

179.

(I) $25^3 \times 49^3$

(II) 35^6

(A) I is greater than II

(B) I is less than II

(C) I is equal to II

(D) None of these

180.

(I) $(11 - 19b^2 - b) + (b^2 - 3b^3 + b) + (3b^2 + 21)$

(II) $32 - 15b^2$

(A) I is greater than II

(B) I is less than II

(C) I is equal to II

(D) None of these

181.

(I) **Pamela saves 15% of her income. If her monthly saving is $600, what is her monthly income?**

(II) **3600**

(A) I is greater than II

(B) I is less than II

(C) I is equal to II

(D) None of these

182.

(I) **Find the ratio of 35 cm to 15 m. (Given, 1 m = 100 cm)**

(II) **7:300**

(A) I is greater than II

(B) I is less than II

(C) I is equal to II

(D) None of these

©All rights reserved-Math-Knots LLC., VA-USA

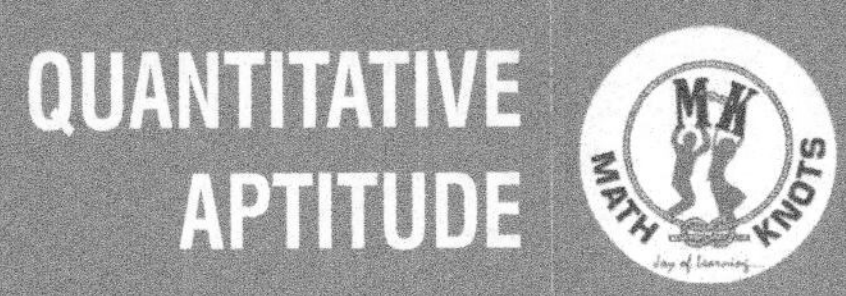

183.

(I) $10^3 + (10^3 - 10^2) + (10^2 - 10) + (10 - 8)$

(II) 1991

(A) I is greater than II

(B) I is less than II

(C) I is equal to II

(D) None of these

184.

(I) In a leap year 72nd day of the year

(II) March 12th

(A) I is greater than II

(B) I is less than II

(C) I is equal to II

(D) None of these

185.

(I) Average of nine 9's

(II) 8

(A) I is greater than II

(B) I is less than II

(C) I is equal to II

(D) None of these

186.

(I) Sum of the Prime numbers between 1 and 10

(II) 19

(A) I is greater than II

(B) I is less than II

(C) I is equal to II

(D) None of these

©All rights reserved-Math-Knots LLC., VA-USA

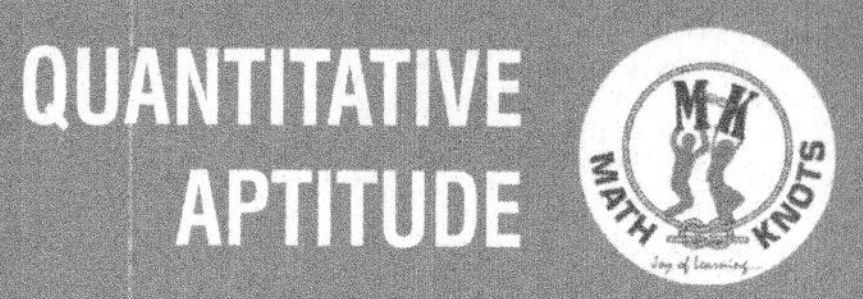

187.

(I) **Length of the side of a square is what percent of its perimeter?**

(II) **20%**

(A) I is greater than II

(B) I is less than II

(C) I is equal to II

(D) None of these

188.

(I) **Number of edges of the cube**

(II) **8**

(A) I is greater than II

(B) I is less than II

(C) I is equal to II

(D) None of these

189.

(I) **Twice the number plus 4 is 18.**

(II) **Number = 9**

(A) I is greater than II

(B) I is less than II

(C) I is equal to II

(D) None of these

190.

(I) **The ratio of the side of a square to its perimeter**

(II) **4:1**

(A) I is greater than II

(B) I is less than II

(C) I is equal to II

(D) None of these

©All rights reserved-Math-Knots LLC., VA-USA

191.

(I) Fifty-five ,55's
(II) 11 X 11 X 25

(A) I is greater than II
(B) I is less than II
(C) I is equal to II
(D) None of these

192.

(I) A bird eats one worm every 5 minutes for an hour.
(II) 10

(A) I is greater than II
(B) I is less than II
(C) I is equal to II
(D) None of these

193.

(I) Sum of two largest primes less than 30
(II) 53

(A) I is greater than II
(B) I is less than II
(C) I is equal to II
(D) None of these

194.

(I) 200 % of 50 %
(II) 100 %

(A) I is greater than II
(B) I is less than II
(C) I is equal to II
(D) None of these

©All rights reserved-Math-Knots LLC., VA-USA

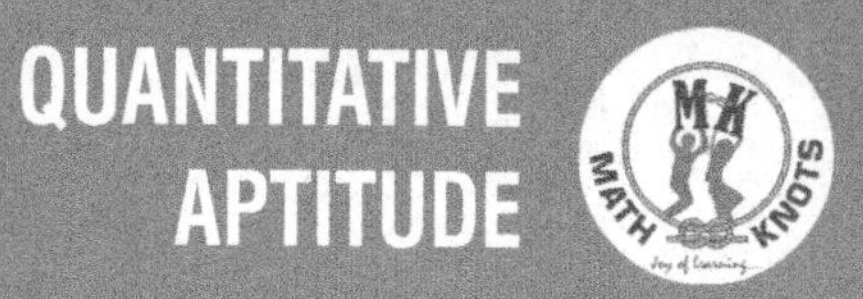

195.

(I) 2019201920192019 ÷ 2019

(II) 1000100010001

(A) I is greater than II   (B) I is less than II

(C) I is equal to II   (D) None of these

196.

(I) $5x = 10y$

(II) $8y = 4x$

(A) I is greater than II   (B) I is less than II

(C) I is equal to II   (D) None of these

197.

(I) $3^{99} + 3^{99} + 3^{99}$

(II) 3^{297}

(A) I is greater than II   (B) I is less than II

(C) I is equal to II   (D) None of these

198.

(I) 2Π

(II) **Length of radius = Side length of Square.**
Area of a Circle / Area of a Square

(A) I is greater than II   (B) I is less than II

(C) I is equal to II   (D) None of these

©All rights reserved-Math-Knots LLC., VA-USA

199.

(I) $33 \times 10 + 33 \times 10^2 + 33 \times 10^3$

(II) 33×1110

(A) I is greater than II (B) I is less than II

(C) I is equal to II (D) None of these

200.

(I) 600 % of One hour in a day

(II) 24 % of One day

(A) I is greater than II (B) I is less than II

(C) I is equal to II (D) None of these

201.

(I) 1999 Quarters

(II) 1999 X 10 Nickel's

(A) I is greater than II (B) I is less than II

(C) I is equal to II (D) None of these

202.

(I) May has how many more seconds than April

(II) 24 X 360 Seconds

(A) I is greater than II (B) I is less than II

(C) I is equal to II (D) None of these

©All rights reserved-Math-Knots LLC., VA-USA

203.

(I) **Average Arithmetic Mean of 2^4, 2^6, 2^8 and 2^{10}**

(II) **2^8**

(A) I is greater than II (B) I is less than II

(C) I is equal to II (D) None of these

204.

(I) **The product of all the integers from -25 to +25 inclusive**

(II) **The sum of all the integers from -25 to 25 inclusive**

(A) I is greater than II (B) I is less than II

(C) I is equal to II (D) None of these

205.

(I) $(1 - \frac{1}{2}) \times (1 - \frac{1}{3}) \times (1 - \frac{1}{4}) \times (1 - \frac{1}{5}) \times (1 - \frac{1}{6})$

(II) $\frac{1}{6}$

(A) I is greater than II (B) I is less than II

(C) I is equal to II (D) None of these

206.

(I) **ab=1 ; a + b**

(II) **2**

(A) I is greater than II (B) I is less than II

(C) I is equal to II (D) None of these

©All rights reserved-Math-Knots LLC., VA-USA

207.

(I) 2 Quaks = 3 Racks and 2 Racks = 3 Darks then 9 Darks = ?

(II) 5 Quaks

(A) I is greater than II

(B) I is less than II

(C) I is equal to II

(D) None of these

208.

(I) Car A can go 5 miles in 7 hours; Car A's average speed

(II) Car B can go 3 miles in 4 hours; Car B's average speed

(A) I is greater than II

(B) I is less than II

(C) I is equal to II

(D) None of these

209.

(I) 80 % of 90 % of Y

(II) 72 % of Y

(A) I is greater than II

(B) I is less than II

(C) I is equal to II

(D) None of these

210.

(I) $a > b > c$; ab

(II) $a > b > c$; ac

(A) I is greater than II

(B) I is less than II

(C) I is equal to II

(D) None of these

©All rights reserved-Math-Knots LLC., VA-USA

211.

(I) $p > 0 ; p (p^2) (p^3)$

(II) $p > 0 ; p + p^2 + p^3$

(A) I is greater than II (B) I is less than II

(C) I is equal to II (D) None of these

212.

(I) $1^3 + 1^5 + 1^1$

(II) $(-1)^2 + (-1)^4 + (-1)^6$

(A) I is greater than II (B) I is less than II

(C) I is equal to II (D) None of these

213.

(I) The time to travel x miles at a speed of y miles per hour

(II) The time to travel 1/y miles at a speed of 1/x miles per hour

(A) I is greater than II (B) I is less than II

(C) I is equal to II (D) None of these

214.

(I) $(5 - x) (5 - x) (5 - x)$

(II) $(x - 5) (x - 5) (x - 5)$

(A) I is greater than II (B) I is less than II

(C) I is equal to II (D) None of these

©All rights reserved-Math-Knots LLC., VA-USA

215.

(I) (-1)(-2) / (-3)

(II) (-1 -2) / -3

(A) I is greater than II
(B) I is less than II
(C) I is equal to II
(D) None of these

216.

a and b are positive integers; $a^b = 64$

(I) a

(II) b

(A) I is greater than II
(B) I is less than II
(C) I is equal to II
(D) None of these

217.

(I) The 12th decimal digit of the fraction 1/8 as a decimal

(II) 5

(A) I is greater than II
(B) I is less than II
(C) I is equal to II
(D) None of these

218.

(I) Ratio of 93 Seconds to 93 Hours

(II) Ratio of 193 Seconds to 193 Hours

(A) I is greater than II
(B) I is less than II
(C) I is equal to II
(D) None of these

©All rights reserved-Math-Knots LLC., VA-USA

219.

(I) $\sqrt{4} + \sqrt{400}$
(II) $\sqrt{40} + \sqrt{4000}$

(A) I is greater than II (B) I is less than II

(C) I is equal to II (D) None of these

220.

(I) $\sqrt{(41^2 - 40^2) / (5^2 - 4^2)}$
(II) 3

(A) I is greater than II (B) I is less than II

(C) I is equal to II (D) None of these

221.

(I) 5 % of 18 % of 2
(II) 2 % of 30 % of 3

(A) I is greater than II (B) I is less than II

(C) I is equal to II (D) None of these

222.

(I) The Area of a square with perimeter 1
(II) The Area of an equilateral triangle with perimeter 1

(A) I is greater than II (B) I is less than II

(C) I is equal to II (D) None of these

©All rights reserved-Math-Knots LLC., VA-USA

223.

(I) $17(21 - 7)$

(II) $7(10 + 4) + 10(4 + 10)$

(A) I is greater than II
(B) I is less than II
(C) I is equal to II
(D) None of these

224.

(I) 2 Minute

(II) 120 Seconds

(A) I is greater than II
(B) I is less than II
(C) I is equal to II
(D) None of these

225.

(I) $(\frac{1}{4})^5$

(II) $(\frac{1}{2})(\frac{1}{3})(\frac{1}{4})(\frac{1}{5})(\frac{1}{6})$

(A) I is greater than II
(B) I is less than II
(C) I is equal to II
(D) None of these

226.

(I) The Average speed of a car going 2 miles in 5 hours.

(II) The Average speed of a car going 1/2 mile in 1/5 hour.

(A) I is greater than II
(B) I is less than II
(C) I is equal to II
(D) None of these

©All rights reserved-Math-Knots LLC., VA-USA

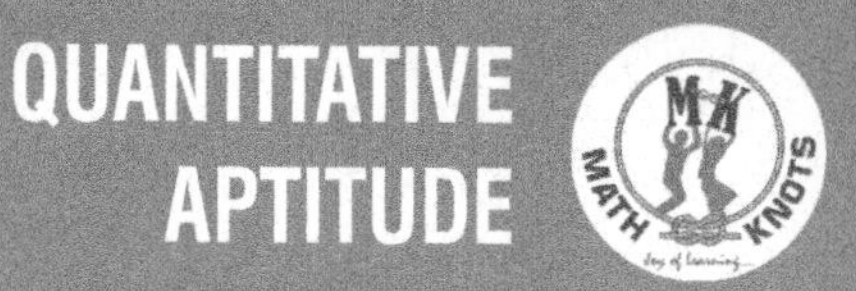

227.

(I) The Number of edges a cube
(II) The Number of vertices a cube

(A) I is greater than II
(B) I is less than II
(C) I is equal to II
(D) None of these

228.

(I) The average of the positive even integers from 2 to 20 inclusive.
(II) The average of the positive odd integers from 1 to 19 inclusive.

(A) I is greater than II
(B) I is less than II
(C) I is equal to II
(D) None of these

229.

(I) The distance traveled at a speed of 50 miles per hour
(II) The distance traveled at a speed of 30 miles per hour

(A) I is greater than II
(B) I is less than II
(C) I is equal to II
(D) None of these

©All rights reserved-Math-Knots LLC., VA-USA

230.

(I) **The smallest four-digit number without repeated digits is subtracted from the largest four digit number without repeated digits, the result is ?**

(II) **8640**

(A) I is greater than II　　(B) I is less than II

(C) I is equal to II　　(D) None of these

231.

(I) **Area of an equilateral triangle with side $\sqrt{3}$**

(II) **$\sqrt{3} / 4$**

(A) I is greater than II　　(B) I is less than II

(C) I is equal to II　　(D) None of these

232.

(I) **Radius of the Circle = Area of the Circle**

(II) **Length of radius = 1 / ∏**

(A) I is greater than II　　(B) I is less than II

(C) I is equal to II　　(D) None of these

©All rights reserved-Math-Knots LLC., VA-USA

233.

(I) How many numbers are in the range of 100 and 400 inclusive contains the digit 3 ?

(II) 136

(A) I is greater than II (B) I is less than II

(C) I is equal to II (D) None of these

234.

(I) What is the 100th digit of the repeating decimal 0. 12367367367367....?

(II) 7

(A) I is greater than II (B) I is less than II

(C) I is equal to II (D) None of these

235.

(I) a % of b = ab / 100

(II) ab/100

(A) I is greater than II (B) I is less than II

(C) I is equal to II (D) None of these

236.

(I) $(1000^2) / (252^2 - 248^2)$

(II) 1000

(A) I is greater than II (B) I is less than II

(C) I is equal to II (D) None of these

©All rights reserved-Math-Knots LLC., VA-USA

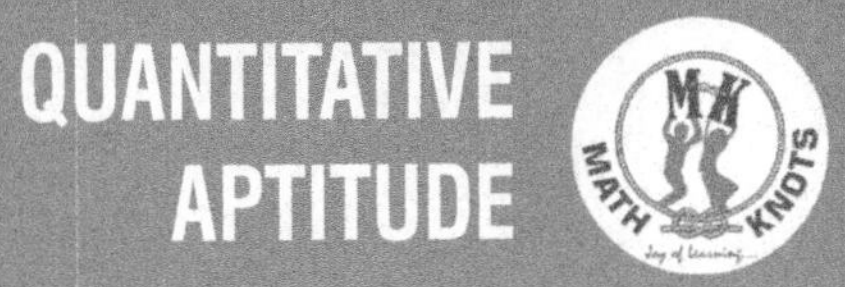

237.

(I) Circumference of a circle
(II) 2 X Area of the circle

(A) I is greater than II
(B) I is less than II
(C) I is equal to II
(D) None of these

238.

(I) 6 dozen pencils cost $8.64
(II) A dozen pencils cost $1.44

(A) I is greater than II
(B) I is less than II
(C) I is equal to II
(D) None of these

239.

(I) A bag of chips cost $0.35
(II) 16 bags of chips cost $5.60

(A) I is greater than II
(B) I is less than II
(C) I is equal to II
(D) None of these

240.

(I) A school has 500 students and 50 teachers. The ratio between the number of teachers and the number of students of the school.

(II) 1:10

(A) I is greater than II
(B) I is less than II
(C) I is equal to II
(D) None of these

241.

(I) **Volume in cubic inches of the container shown in the figure below .**

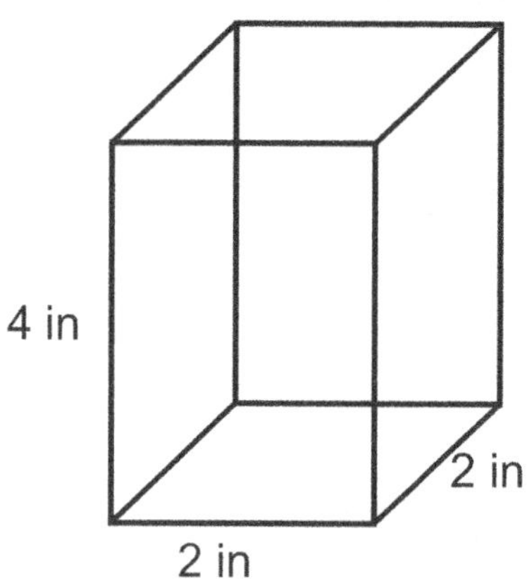

(II) **16 Cubic inches**

(A) I is greater than II

(B) I is less than II

(C) I is equal to II

(D) None of these

242.

(I) **Area in square centimeters of the right triangle in the figure below?**

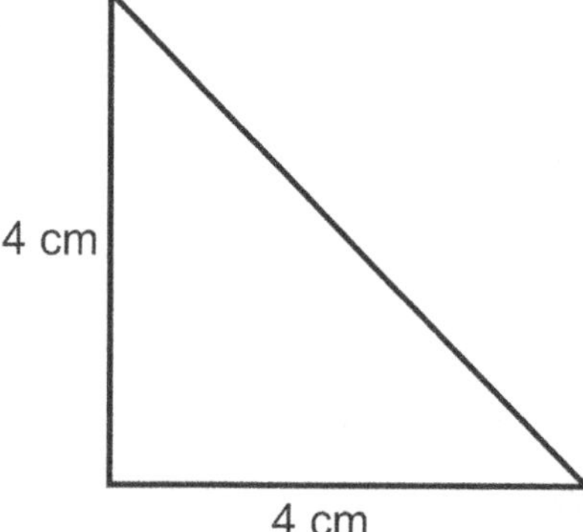

(II) **8 sq.cm**

(A) I is greater than II

(B) I is less than II

(C) I is equal to II

(D) None of these

©All rights reserved-Math-Knots LLC., VA-USA

243.

(I) What percentage of the area of the triangle below is shaded ? All triangles are equilateral.

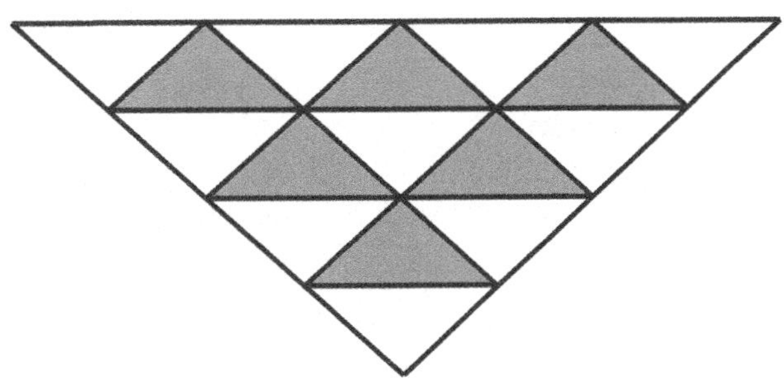

(II) 62.5%

(A) I is greater than II (B) I is less than II

(C) I is equal to II (D) None of these

244.

(I) $(5 + 3)^2 + (5 - 3)^2$

(II) 50 + 18

(A) I is greater than II (B) I is less than II

(C) I is equal to II (D) None of these

245.

(I) Two sides of the right-angled triangle are 4 and 5. What is the length of the third side?

(II) 7 + 2

(A) I is greater than II (B) I is less than II

(C) I is equal to II (D) None of these

©All rights reserved-Math-Knots LLC., VA-USA

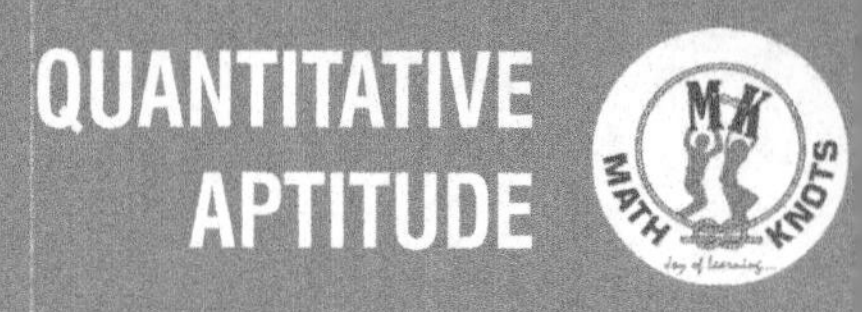

246.

(I) **Two sides of the right-angled triangle are 7 and 24. What is the length of the third side ?**

(II) **5 X 5**

(A) I is greater than II (B) I is less than II

(C) I is equal to II (D) None of these

247.

(I) **What is the slope of the line that passes through the points P(-1,-4) and Q(3,5) ?**

(II) **9/4**

(A) I is greater than II (B) I is less than II

(C) I is equal to II (D) None of these

248.

(I) **If T = U + 7 and U= 11 What is the value of T/4 ?**

(II) **4.5**

(A) I is greater than II (B) I is less than II

(C) I is equal to II (D) None of these

249.

(I) **Slope of the straight line given below**

Y = (-6/5)X + 2/7 ?

(II) **- 6/5**

(A) I is greater than II (B) I is less than II

(C) I is equal to II (D) None of these

©All rights reserved-Math-Knots LLC., VA-USA

250.

(I) Y-intercept of U = 3T+17 ?
(II) 17 / 3

(A) I is greater than II (B) I is less than II

(C) I is equal to II (D) None of these

251.

(I) Distance between numbers (-8) and 10
(II) 2

(A) I is greater than II (B) I is less than II

(C) I is equal to II (D) None of these

252.

(I) Length of the rectangle is 10% more than width.
If the width of the rectangle is 10 cm
What is the area of the rectangle ?
(II) 110 Sq cm

(A) I is greater than II (B) I is less than II

(C) I is equal to II (D) None of these

253.

(I) A cat has 2 cats and each cat then has 4 cats each.
How many legs are there all together ?
(II) 44 legs

(A) I is greater than II (B) I is less than II

(C) I is equal to II (D) None of these

©All rights reserved-Math-Knots LLC., VA-USA

254.

(I) Sam wants to put tiles in her study room. She uses in total of 3750 tiles. There are 75 tiles in each row. How many such rows are there in the study room ?

(II) 10

(A) I is greater than II
(B) I is less than II
(C) I is equal to II
(D) None of these

255.

(I) Zip Zing company is selling their hand bags for $175 which were originally priced as $250. What is percentage of discount offered ?

(II) 35%

(A) I is greater than II
(B) I is less than II
(C) I is equal to II
(D) None of these

256

(I) 10 Decades

(II) 100 Years

(A) I is greater than II
(B) I is less than II
(C) I is equal to II
(D) None of these

©All rights reserved-Math-Knots LLC., VA-USA

257.

(I) 1 Decade
(II) 364 x 10 Days

(A) I is greater than II (B) I is less than II

(C) I is equal to II (D) None of these

258.

(I) Two dice are rolled. The probability that the sum is greater than 3 ?
(II) 11 / 22

(A) I is greater than II (B) I is less than II

(C) I is equal to II (D) None of these

259.

(I) If the length of the Square K is doubled. Then its area increases by ?
(II) 4 times

(A) I is greater than II (B) I is less than II

(C) I is equal to II (D) None of these

©All rights reserved-Math-Knots LLC., VA-USA

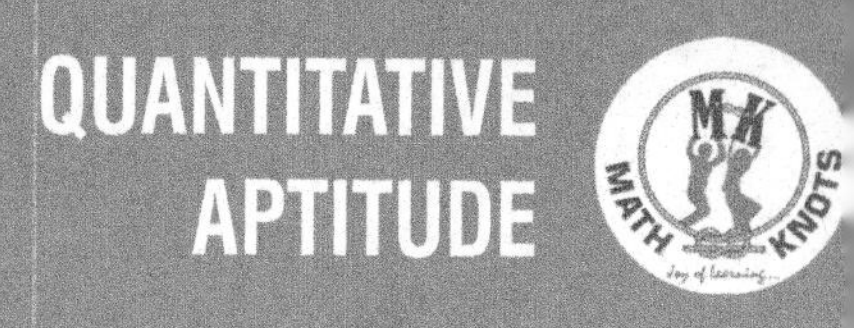

260.

(I) 10 donuts cost $11 There is a 5 % sales tax on the bill. Total bill is ?

(II) $11.55

(A) I is greater than II (B) I is less than II

(C) I is equal to II (D) None of these

261.

(I) Rik solves 1 problem for every 8 sec. How many problems will he solve in 4 minutes ?

(II) 30

(A) I is greater than II (B) I is less than II

(C) I is equal to II (D) None of these

262.

(I) 175 %

(II) 1.75

(A) I is greater than II (B) I is less than II

(C) I is equal to II (D) None of these

263.

(I) 66 + 40

(II) 99 - 19

(A) I is greater than II (B) I is less than II

(C) I is equal to II (D) None of these

©All rights reserved-Math-Knots LLC., VA-USA

264.

(I) A number is divisible by 1 and 29 only. What is the number ?

(II) 29

(A) I is greater than II
(B) I is less than II
(C) I is equal to II
(D) None of these

265.

(I) $990 \div 10000$

(II) 0.099

(A) I is greater than II
(B) I is less than II
(C) I is equal to II
(D) None of these

266.

(I) 1,000,000

(II) 100^3

(A) I is greater than II
(B) I is less than II
(C) I is equal to II
(D) None of these

267.

(I) Greatest Common Factor of 63 and 42 ?

(II) 21

(A) I is greater than II
(B) I is less than II
(C) I is equal to II
(D) None of these

©All rights reserved-Math-Knots LLC., VA-USA

268.

(I) **Area of a Semi Circle**

(II) **$\prod$ X Length of radius X Length of radius X $\frac{1}{2}$**

(A) I is greater than II (B) I is less than II

(C) I is equal to II (D) None of these

269.

(I) **Number of sides of Polygon**

(II) **Number of sides of Decagon**

(A) I is greater than II (B) I is less than II

(C) I is equal to II (D) None of these

270.

(I) **303**

(II) **Sum of the first 3 three-digit natural numbers**

(A) I is greater than II (B) I is less than II

(C) I is equal to II (D) None of these

©All rights reserved-Math-Knots LLC., VA-USA

QUANTITATIVE APTITUDE ANSWER KEYS

©All rights reserved-Math-Knots LLC., VA-USA

©All rights reserved-Math-Knots LLC., VA-USA

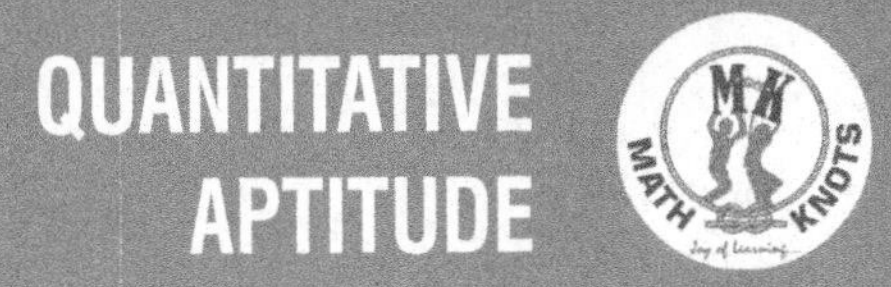

1. C

(I) **Find a number which when divided by 48 gives quotient 20 and remainder 21.**

(II) **981**

Here the Divisor = 48, Quotient = 20 and the Remainder = 21

Dividend = Divisor × Quotient + Remainder
Dividend = 48 × 20 + 21
= 960 + 21
= 981
981 when divided by 48 gives quotient 20 and remainder 21.

2. A

(I) **Find the value of (15625 ÷ 25) ÷ 5**

(II) **120**

First divide 15625 by 25.

```
       6 2 5
    ___________
25) 1 5 6 2 5
   -1 5 0
   ------
       6 2
      -5 0
      ----
       1 2 5
      -1 2 5
      ------
           0
```

Quotient = 625
Remainder = 0
15625 ÷ 25 = 625
Now divide 625 by 5

©All rights reserved-Math-Knots LLC., VA-USA

```
     1  2  5
5) 6  2  5
  -5
   1  2
  -1  0
      2  5
     -2  5
         0
```

So, 625 ÷ 5 = 125

(15625 ÷ 25) ÷ 5 = 125

Answer: **(15625 ÷ 25) ÷ 5 = 125**

3. A

(I) 1016

(II) The population of a city is 56,840. If one out of every 56 people is working in police, how many police personnel are there in the town?

Solution:

Population of a city = 56,840

One out of every 56 people is working in police.

To find: Number of police personnel in the town.

Since out every 56 people there is one police person,

Total number of police personnel = Population of a city ÷ 56

= 56,840 ÷ 56

= 1015

©All rights reserved-Math-Knots LLC., VA-USA

4. B
(I) 0 ÷ 345
(II) 1

Explanation:
If zero is divided by any non zero number, the quotient is zero itself.

0 ÷ 345 = 0

5. C
(I) **Any non-zero whole number divided by itself gives the quotient 1.**
(II) 1

Explanation:
Any non-zero whole number divided by itself gives 1 as the quotient.
Let us verify this by an example.
Example:
Divide 125 by 125

```
        1
125) 1  2  5
    -1  2  5
    ---------
        0
```

Quotient = 1
Remainder = 0

125 ÷ 125 = 1

©All rights reserved-Math-Knots LLC., VA-USA

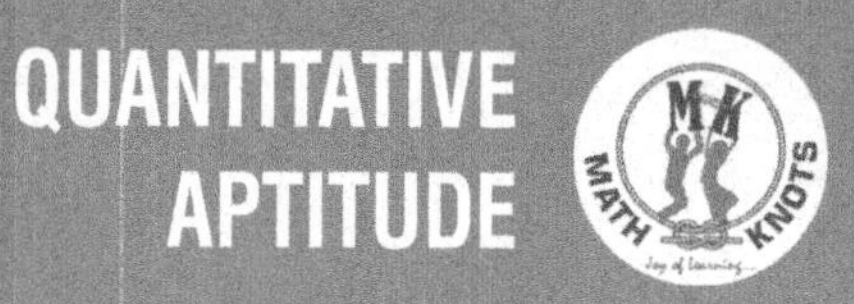

6. **B**

(I) **Length of side of a square whose area is 169 inches^2.**

(II) **23 inches**

Solution:

Area of the square = Side × Side

169 = Side × Side {substituting the value}

13 × 13 = Side × Side

Side = 13

Side of the square = 13 inches

7. **B**

(I) **Length = 12.5 feet**

(II) **Length of a rectangle whose area is 225 ft^2 and width is 9 ft.**

Solution:

Area of the rectangle = Length × Width

225 = Length × 9

225 ÷ 9 = length

{Dividing by 9 on both sides}

25 = Length

Length of the rectangle = 25 ft

©All rights reserved-Math-Knots LLC., VA-USA

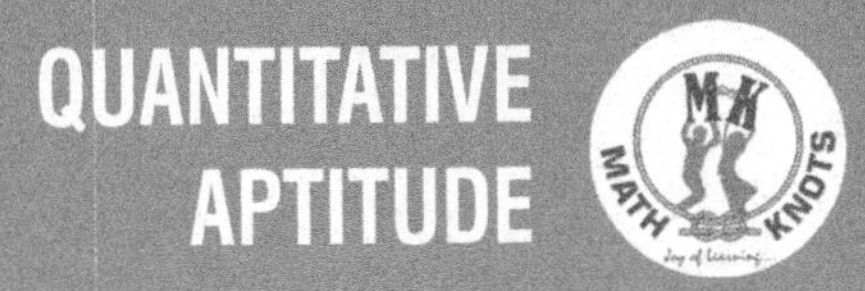

8. A

(I) **Area of a square whose side measures 1.5 inches?**

(II) **2.225 square inches**

Solution:

Area of the square = Side × Side

$= 1.5 \times 1.5 = 2.25$ inches^2

Area of the square = 2.25 inches^2

9. C

(I) **Find the area of a rectangular park whose length is 56 yards and width is 25 yards.**

(II) **14000 yard^2**

Solution:

Area of the rectangular park = Length × Width

$= 56 \times 25 = 1{,}400$ yard^2

Area of the rectangular park = 1,400 yard^2

10. C

(I) **Angles of an isosceles right triangle.**

(II) **Angles are 45°, 45° and 90°**

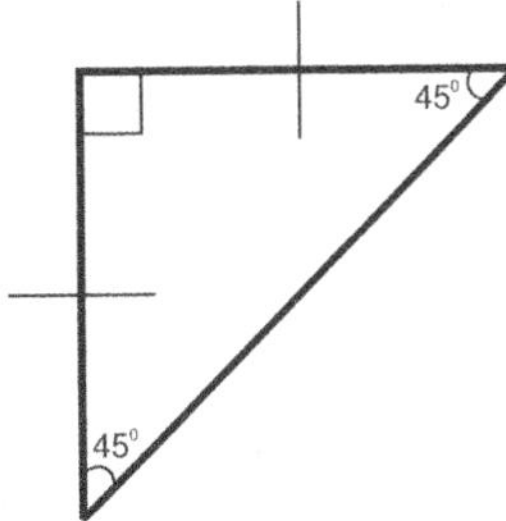

Solution:

A right triangle has one of its angles as 90°.

Since it is an isosceles triangle, the other two angles are equal.

Let the measure of the equal angles be x°.

Now, *sum of the measures of angles of a triangle is 180°.*

$90° + x° + x° = 180°$

$x° + x° = 90°$; $x° = 45°$

©All rights reserved-Math-Knots LLC., VA-USA

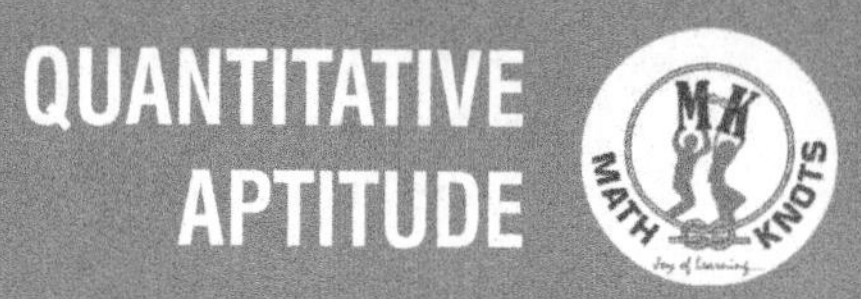

11. A

(I) $2a - 5 = 3$

(II) $a = 3$

$2a - 5 = 3$; $2a = 3 + 5$; $2a = 8$; $a = 4$

12. A

(I) $5x - 8 = 2x - 1$

(II) $x = 2$

$5x - 8 = 2x - 1$; $5x - 2x = 8 - 1$; $3x = 7$; $x = 7 / 3 = 2.3333$

13. B

(I) $(-6) - (+6)$

(II) $(-5) - (+6)$

$(-6) + (-6) = [-6 - 6]$ {opening the bracket}
$= (-12)$ {negative integers are added}
$(-6) - (+6) = -12$
$(-5) + (-6) = [-5 - 6]$ {opening the bracket}
$= (-11)$ {negative integers are added}
$(-5) - (+6) = -11$

14. C

(I) $34 \times 34 \times 34 \times 34 \times 34$

(II) $(34)^5$

If an integer 'a' is multiplied with itself 'k' times, the product is expressed as a^k in exponential/power form.

$34 \times 34 \times 34 \times 34 \times 34 = (34)^5$ {here, 34 is multiplied 5 times}

©All rights reserved-Math-Knots LLC., VA-USA

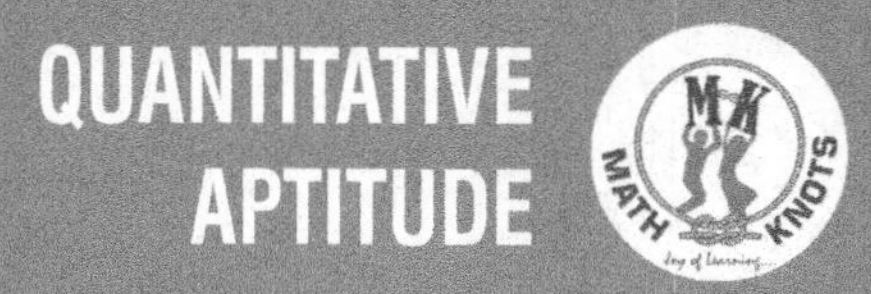

15. A

(I) $(-63)^8$

(II) $(-63) \times (-63) \times (-63) \times (-63) \times (-63) \times (-63) \times (-63)$

Solution:

Concept used: If an integer 'a' is multiplied with itself 'k' times, the product is expressed as a^k in exponential/power form.

So, $(-63) \times (-63) \times (-63) \times (-63) \times (-63) \times (-63) \times (-63) = (-63)^7$

{Here, (-63) is multiplied 7 times}

16. C

(I) 2^4

(II) $4^2 = (2^2)^2 = 2^4$

17. C

(I) $(11)^3 \times (11)^4 \times (11)^{11}$

(II) $(11)^{18}$

$(a)^x \cdot (a)^y \cdot (a)^z = (a)^{x+y+z}$

$(11)^3 \times (11)^4 \times (11)^{11} = (11)^{11+4+3} = (11)^{18}$

18. B

(I) $1{,}000{,}000 \div (-100)$

(II) $-1{,}000$

Solution:

1,000,000 is a positive integer and (-100) is a negative integer.

1,000,000 and (-100) are integers with unlike signs.

The quotient of two integers with unlike signs is negative, obtained by dividing the numerical value of the dividend by the numerical value of the divisor.

$(1{,}000{,}000) \div (-100) = -(1{,}000{,}000 \div 100) = -10{,}000$

©All rights reserved-Math-Knots LLC., VA-USA

19. **B**

(I) **(-84) ÷ ___ = -3**

(II) **38**

Solution:

The required integer is found by dividing (-84) by (-3).
(-84) and (-3) are negative integers.
(-84) and (-3) are integers with like signs.

The quotient of two integers with like signs is positive, obtained by dividing the numerical value of the dividend by the numerical value of the divisor.

(-84) ÷ (-3) = +(84 ÷ 3) = 28

20. **B**

(I) **Divide 0 by -341**

(II) **1**

Solution:

Zero divided by any integer is zero.
0 divided by (-341) is also 0.

21. **A**

(I) **Divide (-135) by (-15)**

(II) **-8**

Solution:

The quotient of two integers with like signs is positive, obtained by dividing the numerical value of the dividend by the numerical value of the divisor.

(-135) ÷ (-15) = (135 ÷ 15) = 9

©All rights reserved-Math-Knots LLC., VA-USA

22. A

(I) 72 ÷ (-9).
(II) -9

Solution:
The given question is 72 ÷ (-9)
72 and (-9) are integers with unlike signs.
The quotient of two integers with unlike signs is negative, obtained by dividing the numerical value of the dividend by the numerical value of the divisor.
(72) ÷ (-9) = -(72 ÷ 9) = -8

23. B

(I) (2826) ÷ (-2)
(II) -1403

Solution:
2826 is a positive integer and (-2) is a negative integer
2826 and (-2) are integers with unlike signs.
(2826) ÷ (-2) = -(2826 ÷ 2) = -1413

24. C

(I) (+912) ÷ (-19)
(II) -48

Explanation:
(+912) is a positive integer and (-19) is a negative integer.
(+912) and (-19) are integers with unlike signs.
(+912) ÷ (-19) = - (912 ÷ 19) = -48

©All rights reserved-Math-Knots LLC., VA-USA

25. B

(I) Simplify: (-2) × [1 - 3 + 6 ÷ (-2)] + 4
(II) 24

(-2) x [1 - 3 + 6 ÷ (-2)] + 4
= (-2) x [1 - 3 + (-3)] + 4
{performing division inside the square bracket}
= (-2) x [1 + (-6)] + 4 {simplifying inside the square bracket}
= (-2) x (-5) + 4 = 10 + 4 = 14

26. C

(I) 345 + 5640 ÷ 10
(II) 909

345 + 5640 ÷ 10 = 345 + 564 = 909 {performing division}

27. A

(I) Simplify: 2 - [3 - {1 - (2 - 3) + 4 - 3 of (1 - 2)}]
(II) 6

2 - [3 - {1 - (2 - 3) + 4 - 3 of (1 - 2)}]
= 2 - [3 - {1 - (2 - 3) + 4 - 3 of (-1)}]
{opening the round bracket (1 - 2)}
= 2 - [3 - {1 - (-1) + 4 - 3 of (-1)}] {opening the round bracket (2 - 3)}
= 2 - [3 - {1 - (-1) + 4 - 3 × (-1)}] {operating 'of'}
= 2 - [3 - {1 - (-1) + 4 - (-3)}] {performing multiplication}
= 2 - [3 - {1 + 1 + 4 + 3}] {simplifying inside the curly bracket}
= 2 - [3 - 9] {opening the curly bracket}
= 2 - (-6) {opening the square bracket}
= 2 + 6
= 8

©All rights reserved-Math-Knots LLC., VA-USA

28. A

(I) Simplify: (-4) + [(2 - 3) + (5 - 3)]

(II) -5

(-4) + [(2 - 3) + (5 - 3)] = (-4) + [(-1) + 2]
= (-4) + 1 = -4 + 1 = -3

29. C

(I) Simplify: (-1) + [5 - {1 - (7 - 3)}]

(II) 7

(-1) + [5 - {1 - (7 - 3)}]

= (-1) + [5 - {1 - 4}] {opening the round brackets}

= (-1) + [5 - (-3)]

= (-1) + [5 + 3] {simplifying inside the square bracket}

= (-1) + 8 = -1 + 8 = 7

30. B

(I) [1 - 3 + {(-4) - 5} - 2]

(II) -11

[1 - 3 + {(-4) - 5} - 2]

= [1 - 3 + {-4 - 5} - 2] {simplifying inside the curly bracket}
= [1 - 3 + (-9) - 2] = [1 - 3 - 9 - 2]
= [1 - 14] {performing addition of negative numbers}
= -13

©All rights reserved-Math-Knots LLC., VA-USA

31. C

(I) (-25) + 5 ÷ (10 - 5)

(II) -24

(-25) + 5 ÷ (10 - 5)
= (-25) + 5 ÷ 5 {opening the round brackets}
= (-25) + 1 {performing division}
= -25 + 1
= -24

32. A

(I) 40 - {30 - 20 - [7 (6 - (2 + 3))]}

(II) 36

Solution: 40 - {30 - 20 - [7 (6 - (2 + 3))]}
= 40 - {30 - 20 - [7 (6 - 5)]} {opening the inner most round bracket}

= 40 - {30 - 20 - [7 x 1]} {opening the next round bracket}

= 40 - {30 - 20 - 7} {opening the square brackets}

= 40 - {10 - 7} {simplifying inside the curly bracket}

= 40 - 3 = 37

33. A

(I) Prime factorization of 5125

(II) 5 x 5 x 41

Solution: 5125 = 5 x 5 x 5 x 41

©All rights reserved-Math-Knots LLC., VA-USA

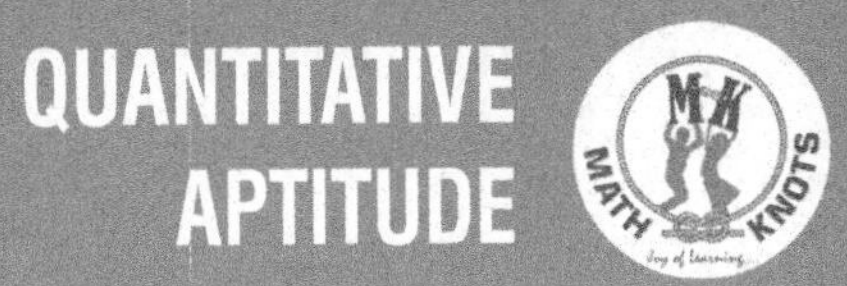

34. C
(I) Prime factorization of 4000.
(II) $2 \times 2 \times 2 \times 2 \times 2 \times 5 \times 5 \times 5$
Solution: $4000 = 2 \times 2 \times 2 \times 2 \times 2 \times 5 \times 5 \times 5$

35. A
(I) Prime factorization of 625
(II) $5 \times 5 \times 5$
Solution: $625 = 5 \times 5 \times 5 \times 5$

36. B
(I) Prime factorization of 450.
(II) $2 \times 3 \times 3 \times 3 \times 5 \times 5$
Solution: $450 = 2 \times 3 \times 3 \times 5 \times 5$

37. C
(I) Prime factorization of 864
(II) $2^5 \times 3^3$
Solution:
Prime factorization of 864 = $2 \times 2 \times 2 \times 2 \times 2 \times 3 \times 3 \times 3 = 2^5 \times 3^3$

38. C
(I) Prime factorization of 252
(II) $2 \times 2 \times 3 \times 3 \times 7$
Solution: $252 = 2 \times 2 \times 3 \times 3 \times 7$

39. B
(I) Sum of the angles of a Triangle = 180^0
(II) Sum of the angles of a Rectangle = 360^0

©All rights reserved-Math-Knots LLC., VA-USA

40. C

(I) **The product of the HCF and LCM of 6 and 12**

(II) **72**

Solution: *The product of any two numbers always equals the product of their LCM and HCF.*

Given that the two numbers are 6 and 12.

product of HCF and LCM = Product of the numbers = 6 x 12 = 72

The product of the HCF and LCM of 6 and 12 is 72.

41. A

(I) **LCM of 54, 60 and 72**

(II) **1006**

Answer: LCM of 54, 60 and 72 = 2 x 3 x 3 x 2 x 3 x 5 x 2 = 1080.

42. A

(I) **The HCF of two numbers is 30 and their product is 5400. Find their LCM.**

(II) **108**

Solution:

The product of any two numbers always equals the product of their LCM and HCF.

We know, for any two numbers,

LCM x HCF = Product of the numbers

LCM x 30 = 5400 {substituting the given values}

LCM = 5400/30 {dividing both sides by 30}

LCM = 180

Thus, the LCM of the given pair of numbers is 180.

©All rights reserved-Math-Knots LLC., VA-USA

43. A

(I) **Largest number that divides 26 and 30 leaving a remainder 2.**

(II) **3**

Solution:

The greatest number which is a common factor of two or more given numbers is called their highest common factor (HCF).

Follow the steps given below to find the required greatest number:

Step 1: Subtract the respective remainders from the numbers.
26 - 2 = 24
30 - 2 = 28
Step 2: Find the HCF of the numbers arrived at step 1 using prime factorization method (as the numbers are small).

Step 3: Find the prime factorization of each of the given numbers.

Step 4: The product of all the common factors, using the least power of each common prime factor is the HCF of the given numbers.

The prime factorizations of the numbers are:
24 = 2 x 2 x 2 x 3
28 = 2 x 2 x7

The product of the common factors = 2 x 2
= 4

HCF of 26, 30= 4

©All rights reserved-Math-Knots LLC., VA-USA

44. B

(I) HCF (highest common factor) of: 154, 140

(II) 24

Solution:

154 = 2 X 7 X 11

140 = 2 X 2 X 5 X 7

HCF of 154 and 140 is 2 X 7 = 14.

45. C

(I) HCF of 300, 350 and 100

(II) 50

Solution:

100 = 2 X 2 X 5 X 5

300 = 3 X 2 X 2 X 5 X 5

350 = 2 X 5 X 5 X 7

The HCF of 300, 350 and 100 is 2 X 5 X 5 = 50.

46. D

(I) Common factors of 4, 12 and 16

(II) 1, 2 and 3.

Solution: All the common factors of 4, 12 and 16 are 1, 2 and 4.

47. B

(I) The smallest multiple of 16

(II) 32

Answer: The smallest multiple of 16 is <u>16 is itself</u>

48. C

(I) The greatest factor of any number is the number itself

(II) The number itself

©All rights reserved-Math-Knots LLC., VA-USA

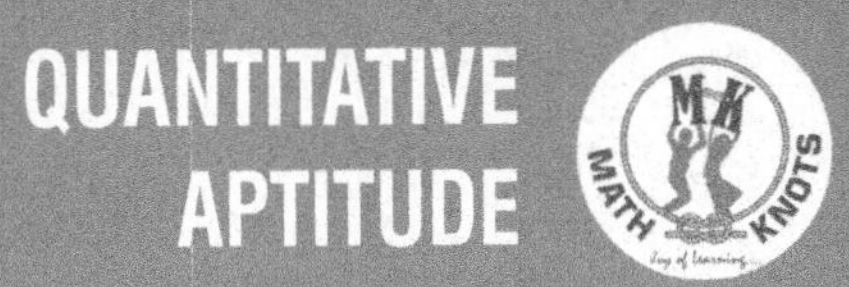

49. B

50. A

(I) Supplementary angles

(II) $80° + 50°$

Two angles are said to be a pair of supplementary angles if the sum of their measures is equal to 180°.

51. C

(I) Supplementary angles

(II) $90° + 90° = 180°$

Two angles are said to be a pair of supplementary angles if the sum of their measures is equal to 180°.

52. C

(I) Complementary angle

(II) $45° + 45° = 90°$

Two angles are said to be a pair of complementary angles if the sum of their measures is equal to 90°.

53. C

(I) Subtract $(x^2 + 2x - 3)$ from $(10 - 3x)$.

(II) $(13 - 5x - x^2)$

Solution: On subtracting $(x^2 + 2x - 3)$ from $(10 - 3x)$ we get $(13 - 5x - x^2)$.

$$\begin{array}{rl} & 10 - 3x + 0 \\ (+) & \underline{3 - 2x - x^2} \\ & \underline{13 - 5x - x^2} \end{array}$$

©All rights reserved-Math-Knots LLC., VA-USA

54. C

(I) 8 less than 21 decreased by a

(II) (21 - a) - 8

Solution:

Given variable = 'a'

21 decreased by 'a' means that 'a' is subtracted from 21.

So, 21 decreased by 'a'= 21 - a

8 less than this difference = (21 - a) - 8

55. A

(I) Coefficient of x in $(4x + 3y^2)$ is 4

(II) 3

56. A

(I) 3 more than x is X + 3

(II) x - 3

57. C

(I) Twice the sum of x and y

(II) 2 (x + y).

Solution:

Given variables are 'x' and 'y'.

Sum of 'x' and 'y' = x + y

Twice the sum of 'x' and 'y' = 2 × (x + y)

= 2 (x + y)

©All rights reserved-Math-Knots LLC., VA-USA

58. B

(I) If $p = 2$ and $q = -3$, find the value of $p^2 - q^2$

(II) -4

Solution:

Given expression: $p^2 - q^2$

To find: The value of the above expression when $p = 2$ and $q = -3$

On substituting $p = 2$ and $q = -3$ in the given expression, we get,

$p^2 - q^2 = (2)^2 - (-3)^2$

$= 4 - 9 = -5$

59. C

(I) If $x = 3/5$ and $y = -5/7$, find the value $(x/y)^2$

(II) $(21/25)^2$

On substituting $x = 3/5$ and $y = -5/7$ in the given expression, we get,

$$\left(\frac{x}{y}\right)^2 = \left(\frac{\frac{3}{5}}{\frac{-5}{7}}\right)^2$$

$$= \left(\frac{3}{5} \times \frac{7}{-5}\right)^2 = \left(\frac{21}{-25}\right)^2$$

$$= \left(\frac{21 \times 21}{-25 \times -25}\right) = \frac{441}{625} = \left(\frac{21}{25}\right)^2 \qquad \{(-) \times (-) = (+)\}$$

60. A

(I) If $x = 1$, $y = 2$, $z = 0$ find the value of $(x + y)^2 + z^2$

(II) 5

On substituting $x = 1$, $y = 2$ and $z = 0$ in the given expression, we get,

$(x + y)^2 + z^2 = (1 + 2)^2 + (0)^2 = 3^2 + 0 = 9 + 0 = 9$

©All rights reserved-Math-Knots LLC., VA-USA

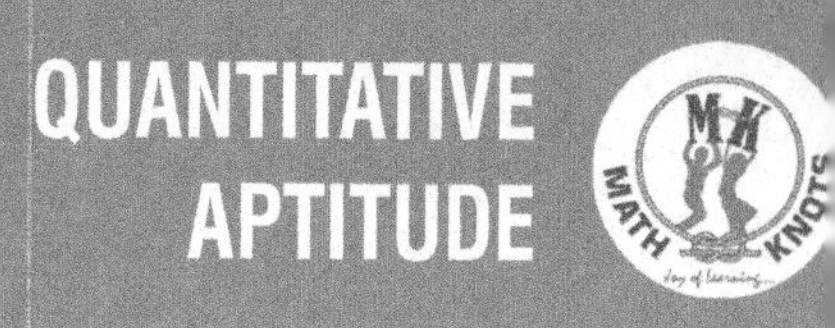

61. B

(I) Range of the data : 2.4, 3.1, 2.8, 2.0, 2.7, 3.3, 2.6

(II) 1.5

Range is the difference between the highest and the lowest value.

Range of the given data = 3.3 mm - 2.0 mm

= 1.3 mm

62. C

(I) $\frac{(5^{-2})^3}{5^3}$

(II) 5^{-9}

Solution:

$$\frac{(5^{-2})^3}{5^3} = \frac{5^{-2\times3}}{5^3} = \frac{5^{-6}}{5^3} = 5^{-6-3} = 5^{-9}$$ $\{(a^p)^q = a^{p \times q}\}$

63. A

(I) $9^{(-5/2 + 3/2 - 1/2)}$

(II) $9^{-3} = (3^2)^{-3} = 3^{-6} = \frac{1}{3^6}$

Solution:

$9^{(-5/2 + 3/2 - 1/2)} = 9^{(-5 + 3 - 1)/2}$

$= 9^{-3/2} = (3^2)^{-3/2}$ {9 = 3^2, by prime factorization}

$= (3)^{2 \times (-3/2)} = 3^{-3}$ $\{[(a^p)^q] = a^{pq}\}$

$= \frac{1}{3^3} = \frac{1}{27}$

©All rights reserved-Math-Knots LLC., VA-USA

64. C

(I) $\sqrt{225} = 15$

(II) 15

65. A

(I) **Find the smallest number with which 147 must be multiplied to get a perfect square.**

(II) 2

Solution:

A given number is a perfect square if it is expressible as the product of pairs of equal factors.

$147 \times 3 = \underline{3 \times 3} \times \underline{7 \times 7}$

or, $441 = \underline{3 \times 3} \times \underline{7 \times 7}$

$\sqrt{441} = 3 \times 7$

$= 21$

66. B

(I) $(2^3)^{-2}$

(II) 2^6

Solution : $(2^3)^{-2} = 2^{3\times(-2)} = 2^{-6}$

67. B

(I) **Find the value of x, if $5^x \times 3^x = 50625$**

(II) 8

$5^x \times 3^x = 50625$

$(5 \times 3)^x = 50625$ $\{(a \times b)^p = a^p \times b^p\}$

$15^x = 50625$

By prime factorization,

$50625 = 3 \times 3 \times 3 \times 3 \times 5 \times 5 \times 5 \times 5$

$= 3^4 \times 5^4 = (3 \times 5)^4 = 15^4$

$15^x = 50625 = 15^x = (15)^4$; $x = 4$ $\{\text{if } a^p = a^q \text{, then } p = q\}$

©All rights reserved-Math-Knots LLC., VA-USA

68. C

(I) $(9)^3 \times (9)^{-6}$

(II) $(9)^{-3}$

$(9)^3 \times (9)^{-6} = (9)^{3+(-6)} = (9)^{(-3)}$ $\{a^p \times a^q = (a)^{p+q}\}$

69. B

(I) Simplify: $(3^3)^{-2}$

(II) 3

$(3^3)^{-2} = (3)^{3\times(-2)} = (3)^{(-6)}$ $\{(a^p)^q = a^{p\times q}\}$

70. B

(I) ABCD is a rhombus with ∟DCB = 38°. Find ∟CAB.

(II) 92

In a rhombus, opposite angles are equal.

A = C = 38°

∟*CAB = 38°/2 = 19°*

©All rights reserved-Math-Knots LLC., VA-USA

71. **A**

(I) ABCD is a rectangle with ∟BAC = 22°. Determine ∟DBC.

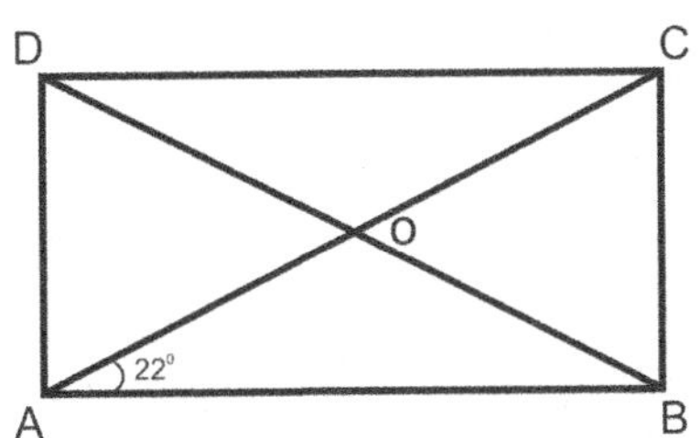

(II) ∟DBC = 22°

We know,

Diagonals of a rectangle are equal and they bisect each other.

AO = OB

Triangle AOB is an isosceles triangle.

∟BAO = ∟ABO = 22°

∟ABO = 22°

Also, all angles of the rectangle are right angles.

∟ABC = 90°

∟ABD + ∟DBC = 90°

∟ABO + ∟DBC = 90°

22°+ ∟DBC = 90°

∟DBC = 90°- 22°

∟DBC = 68°

©All rights reserved-Math-Knots LLC., VA-USA

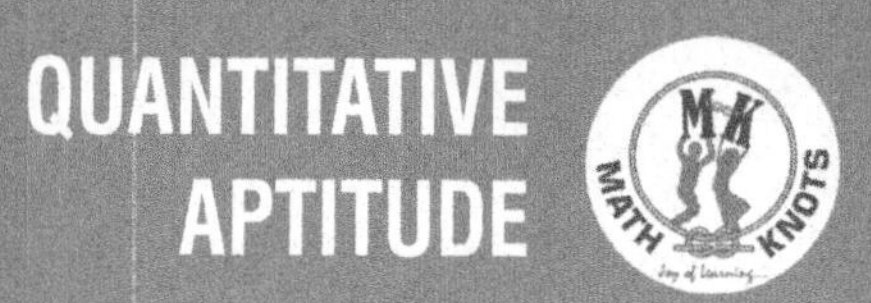

72. C

(I) O is the center of the given circle. If ∟XYZ = 80°, find the measure of ∟XOZ.

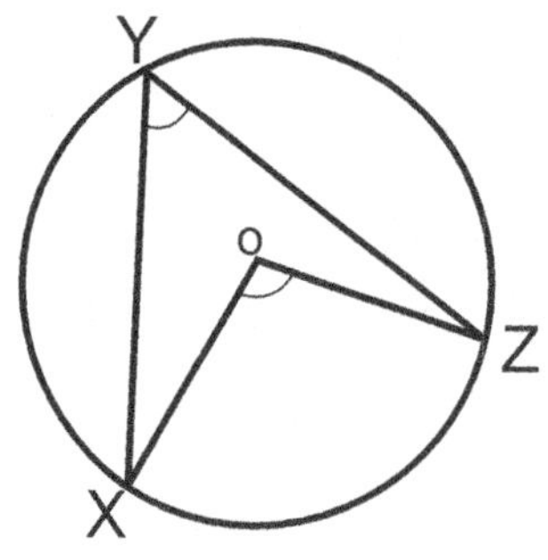

(II) ∟XOZ = 160°,

∟XYZ = 80°

To find: The measure of ∟XOZ

Solution:

Arc XZ subtends ∟XOZ at the center of the circle and ∟XYZ at the circumference of the circle.

∟XOZ = 2∟XYZ

{Angle subtended by an arc of a circle at the center is double the angle subtended by it at any point on the remaining part of the circumference}

∟XOZ = 2 x 80°

∟XOZ = 160°

The measure of ∟XOZ = 160°

©All rights reserved-Math-Knots LLC., VA-USA

73. A

(I) PQRS is a cyclic quadrilateral. If $\angle S = 82°$ and $\angle P = 98°$, find Q.

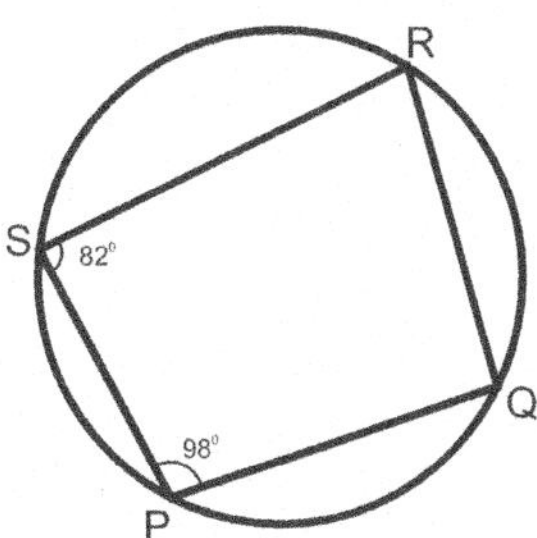

(II) $\angle Q = 82°$

PQRS is a cyclic quadrilateral.
$\angle S = 82°$ and $\angle P = 98°$

To find: The measure of $\angle Q$
Opposite angles of a cyclic quadrilateral are supplementary

$\angle Q + \angle S = 180°$
$\angle Q + 82° = 180°$
$\angle Q = 180° - 82°$
$\angle Q = 98°$

©All rights reserved-Math-Knots LLC., VA-USA

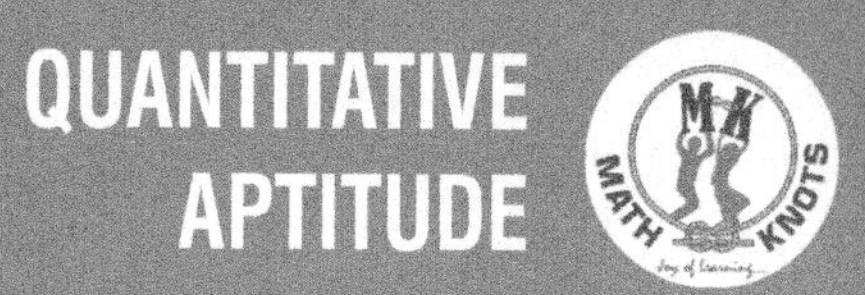

74. B

(I) **A field is in the form of triangle with area 3 hectare. If length of its base is 200 meters, find its altitude.**

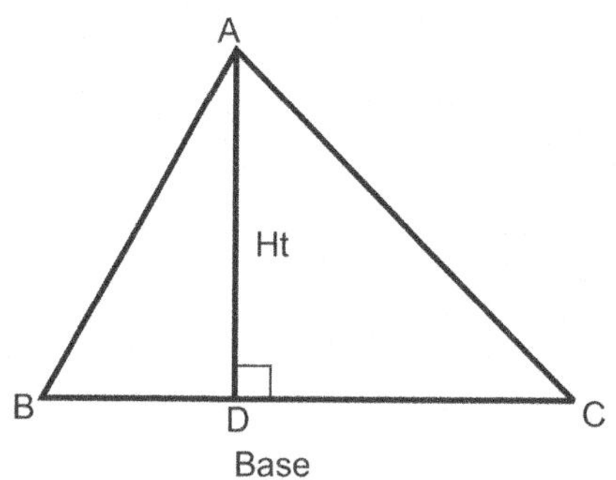

(II) **3000 Meters**

Base of the triangle = 200 m

Area of the triangle = 3 hectare

= 30000 m^2 {1 Hectare = 10000 m^2}

Area of the triangle = ½ base x height ⇒ 30000 = ½ b x h

$$30000 = \frac{1}{2} \times 200 \times h$$

$$\text{Or, } h = \frac{30000 \times 2}{200.}$$

h = 300

Height = 300 Meters

©All rights reserved-Math-Knots LLC., VA-USA

75. C

(I) **The parallel sides of a trapezium are 10 inches and 15 inches in length. The distance between these sides is 8 inches. Find the area of the trapezium.**

(II) **100 inches^2**

Solution:

Area of the trapezium = $\frac{1}{2}$ × (sum of parallel sides) × (distance between them)

$$= \frac{1}{2} \times (10 + 15) \times 8$$

$$= \frac{1}{2} \times (25) \times 8$$

$$= 25 \times 4$$

$$= 100 \text{ inches}^2$$

76. A

(I) **The area of a trapezium is 351 ft^2. If the parallel sides of the trapezium measure 17 ft and 22 ft respectively, find the height of the trapezium.**

(II) **17 ft.**

Solution:

Area of the trapezium = $\frac{1}{2}$ × (sum of parallel sides) × (distance between them)

$351 = \frac{1}{2} \times (17 + 22) \times h$

$351 \times 2 = 39h$

$702 = 39h$

$h = 18$ feet

©All rights reserved-Math-Knots LLC., VA-USA

77. **A**

(I) **15**

(II) **The area of rhombus is 119 inches^2 and its perimeter is 56 inches. Find its altitude.**

Area of rhombus = base × height
Perimeter of the rhombus = 4 ×side

Solution: Let the side of rhombus be 'a' inches.
Perimeter of rhombus = 4 × side = 4a
56 = 4a
14 = a
height = area /side = 119/14 = 8.5 inches

78. **C**

(I) **Area of a rhombus whose diagonals measure 15 inches and 21 inches.**

(II) **157.5 inches^2**

Area of rhombus = $\frac{1}{2}$ × (product of diagonals)

$= \frac{1}{2} \times d_1 \times d_2$

$= \frac{1}{2} \times 15 \times 21$

= 157.5 inches^2

©All rights reserved-Math-Knots LLC., VA-USA

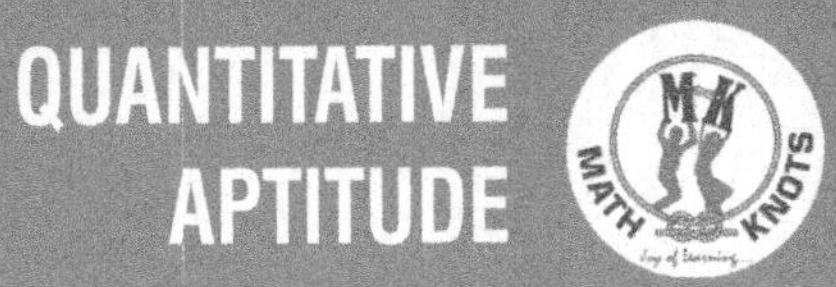

79. C

(I) **The radius of a circle whose area is 2,464 ft^2**

(II) **28 ft.**

Area of the circle = 2464 ft^2 = Πr^2

$$r^2 = \frac{2464}{\Pi}$$

$$r^2 = \frac{2464}{22/7}$$

$$r^2 = \frac{2464 \times 7}{22}$$

$$r^2 = 784$$

$$r = \sqrt{784}$$

$$r = 28 \text{ ft}$$

80. B

(I) **The circumference of a circle whose radius is 21 inches. (Take, Π = 22/7)**

(II) **136 inches**

The circumference of the circle (c) = $2\Pi r$

$$= 2 \times \frac{22}{7} \times 21$$

$$= 2 \times 22 \times 3$$

$$= 132 \text{ inches}$$

©All rights reserved-Math-Knots LLC., VA-USA

81. C

(I) The area of a circle whose diameter is 8.4 inches. (Consider, π = 22/7)

(II) 55.44 inches^2

Diameter (d) of the circle = 8.4 inches

Radius (r) of the circle = d/2

= 8.4/2 inches

= 4.2 inches

The area of the circle (A) = Πr^2

$= \frac{22}{7} \times 4.2 \times 4.2$

= 55.44 inches^2

82. B

(I) Cube root of (- 729/4913).

(II) (9/17)

We know, $\frac{\sqrt[3]{a}}{\sqrt[3]{b}} = \sqrt[3]{\frac{a}{b}}$

$$\sqrt[3]{\frac{(-729)}{4913}} = \frac{\sqrt[3]{(-729)}}{\sqrt[3]{4913}}$$

To find their cube roots, resolve (-729) and 4913 as a product of prime factors and make triplets of similar factors.

(-729) = -(3 x 3 x 3 x 3 x 3 x 3)

$\sqrt[3]{-729}$ = - (3 x 3)

= -9

©All rights reserved-Math-Knots LLC., VA-USA

$4913 = \underline{17 \times 17 \times 17}$

$\sqrt[3]{4913} = 17$

$\sqrt[3]{\frac{-729}{4913}} = \frac{-9}{17}$

83. **C**

(I) **In the figure given below, AB || CD and MN is a transversal line. Find the unknown angle.**

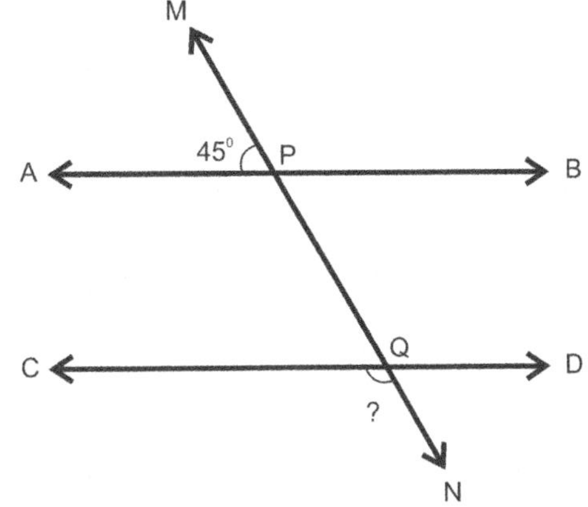

(II) **135°.**

Let P & Q be the points of intersection of lines AB, CD & the transversal MN.

Now, AB || CD and MN is the transversal.

∟APM = ∟PQC = 45°{Corresponding angles are equal}

Or, PQC = 45°......(1)

Also, ∟CQN + ∟PQC = 180° {linear pair}

∟CQN + 45°= 180° {from (1)}

∟CQN = 180° - 45°

∟CQN = 135°

©All rights reserved-Math-Knots LLC., VA-USA

84. C

(I) Between 12 PM to 5.10 PM hours hand has turned through an angle

(II) 155°

Solution: 5 Hours and 10 Minutes is 31/6 hours

In one hour the hours hand travels 360/12 = 60°

In 31/6 Hoursit travels (31/6) X 60° = 155°

85. A

(I) How many times does the hands of a clock make right angle in a day?

(II) 22

Solution: In 12 hours the hands of the clock are 22 times in right angle position.

In a day there are 24 hours so, right angle is formed 44 times.

86. C

(I) Letters of the word APPLE can be arranged in how many ways?

(II) 60

Solution: The word APPLE contains 5 letters 1A ,2P.1L,1E

Required number of ways = 5! / (1!) (2!) (1!) (1!)

= 5 X 4 X 3 X 2 X 1 /2 = 60 ways

87. A

(I) Probability of getting a number greater than 4, when a dice is rolled

(II) 1/4

Solution: Possible outcomes are 5 & 6 out of the possibilities

1 , 2 , 3 , 4 , 5 , 6

Probability is 2 / 6 = 1 / 3

©All rights reserved-Math-Knots LLC., VA-USA

88. B

(I) Volume of the box with dimensions 0.8 inches X 0.6 inches X 2.5 inches

(II) 4.50 Cubic inches

Solution:

0.8 inches X 0.6 inches X 2.5 inches = 1.2 Cubic inches

89. A

(I) Find | x - y |, when x = (- 5) and y = (-11/5)

(II) (-14/5)

$$| x - y | = \left|(-5)-\left(\frac{-11}{5}\right)\right|$$

$$= \left|\left(\frac{-5\times5}{1\times5}\right)-\left(\frac{-11}{5}\right)\right|$$ {LCM of the denominators 1 & 5 is 5}

$$= \left|\left(\frac{-25}{5}\right)-\left(\frac{-11}{5}\right)\right|$$

$$= \left|\frac{-25-(-11)}{5}\right|$$

$$= \left|\frac{-25+11}{5}\right|$$

$$= \left|\frac{-14}{5}\right|$$

$$= \frac{14}{5}$$ *{Absolute value is the positive numerical value of a number}*

©All rights reserved-Math-Knots LLC., VA-USA

90. *C*

(I) $\left|\left(\frac{-9}{7}\right)+\left(\frac{-11}{3}\right)\right|$

(II) $\frac{104}{21}$

$$\left|\left(\frac{-9}{7}\right)+\left(\frac{-11}{3}\right)\right| = \left|\left(\frac{-9\times 3}{7\times 3}\right)+\left(\frac{-11\times 7}{3\times 7}\right)\right|$$ {LCM of the denominators 7 & 3 is 21}

$$= \left|\left(\frac{-27}{21}\right)+\left(\frac{-77}{21}\right)\right|$$

$$= \left|\frac{-27-77}{21}\right|$$

$$= \left|\frac{-104}{21}\right|$$

$$= \frac{104}{21}$$ {*Absolute value is the positive numerical value of a number*}

$$\left|\left(\frac{-9}{7}\right)+\left(\frac{-11}{3}\right)\right| = \frac{104}{21}$$

©All rights reserved-Math-Knots LLC., VA-USA

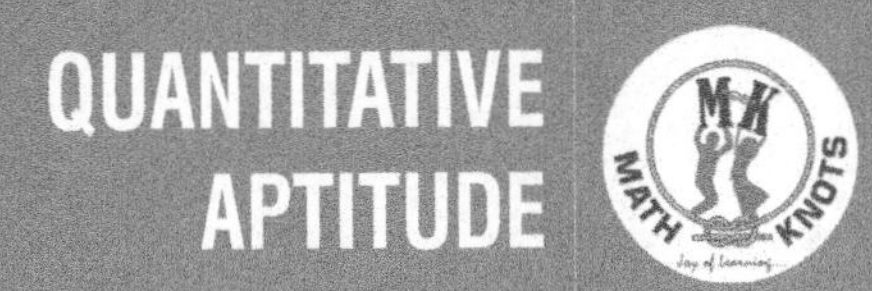

91. B

(I) $\left(\frac{-1}{8}\right)^{(-1)}$

(II) 8

Here the power is (-1), so $\left(\frac{-1}{8}\right)^{(-1)}$ is same as the reciprocal of $\left(\frac{-1}{8}\right)$

The reciprocal of $\frac{p}{q}$ *is* $\frac{q}{p}$ *i.e.* $\left(\frac{p}{q}\right)^{(-1)} = \frac{q}{p}$

p = -1, q = 8

The reciprocal of $\left(\frac{-1}{8}\right) = \frac{8}{-1}$

$\frac{8}{-1}$ = (-8) {Bringing negative sign to numerator}

$\left(\frac{8}{-1}\right)$ = (-8)

92. C

(I) $\left(\frac{3}{-5}\right)^{3}$

(II) $\frac{-27}{125}$

$\left(\frac{3}{-5}\right)^{3} = \frac{3^3}{(-5)^3}$

$\frac{3 \times 3 \times 3}{(-5) \times (-5) \times (-5)} = \frac{27}{-125} = \frac{-27}{125}$

$\left(\frac{3}{-5}\right)^{3} = \frac{-27}{125}$

©All rights reserved-Math-Knots LLC., VA-USA

93. B

(I) Express $\frac{-81}{256}$ in exponential form.

(II) $\left(\frac{3}{4}\right)^4$

Solution:

$\frac{-81}{256} = -\left(\frac{81}{256}\right)$

$\left(\frac{81}{256}\right) = \frac{3 \times 3 \times 3 \times 3}{2 \times 2 \times 2 \times 2 \times 2 \times 2 \times 2 \times 2}$

$= \frac{3^4}{2^8}$

$= \frac{3^4}{2^{2 \times 4}}$

$= \frac{3^4}{(2^2)^4}$

$= \frac{3^4}{(2 \times 2)^4}$

$= \frac{3^4}{(4)^4} = \left(\frac{3}{4}\right)^4$

$\frac{-81}{256} = -\left(\frac{81}{256}\right) = -\left(\frac{3}{4}\right)^4$

©All rights reserved-Math-Knots LLC., VA-USA

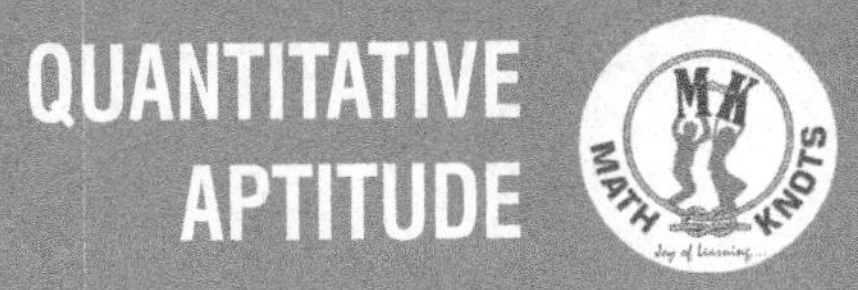

94. A

(I) Earth's circumference is 4×10^4 km. What is its circumference in meters?

(II) 40,000,00 meters.

Solution:

Earth's circumference = 4×10^4 km We know, 1 km = 1000 m.

$4 \times 10^4 km = 4 \times 10^4 \times 1000 m$

$= 4 \times 10^4 \times 10^3 m = 4 \times 10^{4+3} m = 4 \times 10^7 m$ $\{a^m \times a^n = a^{m+n}\}$

Expressing the above number in usual form we have,

$4 \times 10^7 m = 4 \times 10{,}000{,}000\ m = 40{,}000{,}000\ m$

Earth's circumference = 40,000,000 m

Earth's circumference is 40,000,000 meters.

95. B

(I) 11.2×10^{-6}

(II) 0.000112

Expressing the given number in usual form we get,

11.2 / 1000000 = 0.0000112 ; $11.2 \times 10^{-6} = 0.0000112$

96. A

(I) GCF of 12 and 54

(II) 3

GCF of 12 and 54 is 6

97. B

(I) 11

(II) GCF of 66 and 22

GCF of 66 and 22 is 22

©All rights reserved-Math-Knots LLC., VA-USA

98. C

(I) 66.01 X 2.22

(II) (66 + 0.01) X (2 + 0.22) = 66.01 X 2.22

99. B

(I) Least common Multiple of 3 and 7

(II) ∏ X 7

Least common Multiple of 3 and 7 is 21

∏ X 7 = (22 / 7) x 7 = 22

©All rights reserved-Math-Knots LLC., VA-USA

100. B
(I) Area of a Circle X 1/2
(II) ∏ X Length of radius X Length of radius

101. A
(I) 5^5
(II) 625

102. C
(I) Least Common Multiple (LCM) of 6 and 9 is 18
(II) 9 X 2

103. B
(I) 55 meters below sea level
(II) 55 meters

104. C
(I) 9° below zero
(II) -9°

105. B
(I) 19° below freezing point
(II) -18^0

©All rights reserved-Math-Knots LLC., VA-USA

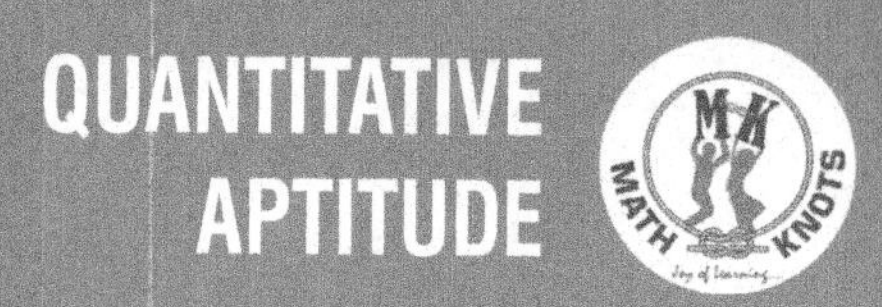

106. A
(I) 88 % = 88 / 100
(II) 0.80 = 80 / 100

107. B
(I) Debt of one thousand dollars and 9 cents
(II) 1000.09

108. A
(I) Elevation of 5505.25 feet above sea level
(II) -5505.25

109. A
(I) Gain of $55.45
(II) - 55.40

110. C
(I) Area of the Circle / Perimeter of the Circle
(II) Radius / 2

Solution:
Area of the Circle / Perimeter of the Circle
= ∏ X Length of radius X Length of radius / 2∏ X Length of radius
= Length of radius/ 2

111. B
(I) Loss of $3333 is -$3333
(II) $3333

©All rights reserved-Math-Knots LLC., VA-USA

112. C
(I) Loss of \$9842.99 is -\$9842.99
(II) -\$9842.99

113. A
(I) Gain of \$1,000,050
(II) \$1,000,000

114. C
(I) Reciprocal of 2/3 is 3/2
(II) 3/2

115. A
(I) | -0.89 | = 0.89
(II) - 0.88

116. C
(I) Opposite of 999 is -999
(II) -999

117. B
(I) Additive Identity is Zero
(II) 1

118. C
(I) Multiplicative Identity is one.
(II) 1

119. C
(I) (7a + 11) + (9a - 4) = 16a + 7
(II) 16a + 7

©All rights reserved-Math-Knots LLC., VA-USA

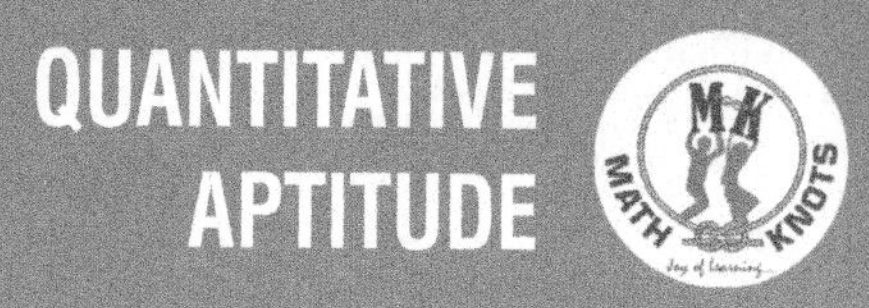

120. A

(I) $8(a - 3) + 11(a + 14) = 8a - 24 + 11a + 154 = 19a + 130$

(II) $19a - 24$ (where a is a whole number)

121. A

(I) Area of triangle with base as 9 units and height as 5 units = 9 x 5 / 2 = 45 / 2 = 22.5

(II) 12.5 square units

122. C

(I) Mean of 31, 31, 37, 34,35

(II) 33.6

(31 + 31 + 37 + 34 + 35) / 5 = 33.6

123. A

(I) Area of Square with a side length of 11 inches = 11 X 11 = 121 Sq.inches

(II) 120 inches

124. A

(I) Area = 92 square feet

(II) Area of Square with a side length of 8 feet = 64 square feet

125. C

(I) Area of Rectangle with a side of length of 5 units and 4 units = 5 X 4 = 20 sq.units

(II) 10 X 2 sq.units= 20 sq.units

©All rights reserved-Math-Knots LLC., VA-USA

126. A

(I) John buys toffees at the rate of 4 for a dollar and sells them at the rate of 3 for a dollar. Find his profit in percent.

(II) 33.303 %

Gain = Selling price - Cost price

$$\text{Gain\%} = \frac{\text{Gain}}{\text{Cost Price}} \times 100$$

Cost Price of 4 toffees = \$1

Cost Price of 1 toffee = $\$\frac{1}{4}$

Selling price of 3 toffees = \$1

Selling price of 1 toffee = $\$\frac{1}{3}$

Gain = Selling Price - Cost Price

$$= \$\frac{1}{3} - \$\frac{1}{4}$$

$$\frac{4}{12} - \frac{3}{12} = \frac{4-3}{12} = \frac{1}{12}$$

$$\text{Gain\%} = \frac{\text{Gain}}{\text{Cost Price}} \times 100$$

$$= \frac{\$\frac{1}{12}}{\$\frac{1}{4}} \times 100 = \frac{1}{12} \times \frac{4}{1} \times 100$$

$$= \frac{400}{12} = \frac{100}{3}$$

Gain % = 33.33%

©All rights reserved-Math-Knots LLC., VA-USA

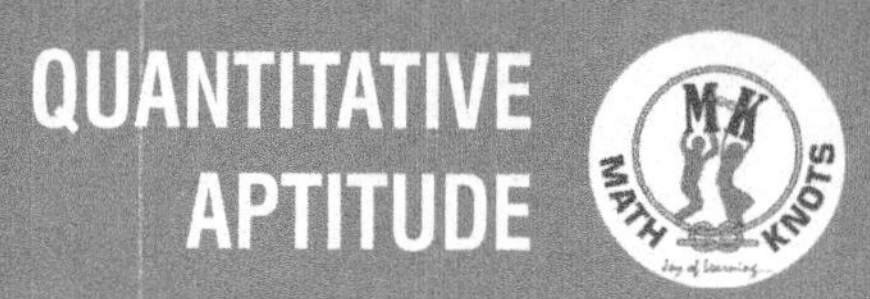

127. C

(I) **An electrician sells a room heater for $342, gaining 1/5th of its cost price. Find his profit in percent.**

(II) **20%**

Selling price of room heater = $342

Let the Cost Price of heater = $x

Gain earned = $\left(\frac{1}{5}\right)X$

To find: Gain percent = ?

Formulae used: $\text{Gain\%} = \frac{\text{Gain}}{\text{Cost Price}} \times 100$

$$\text{Gain\%} = \frac{\text{Gain}}{\text{Cost Price}} \times 100$$

$$= \frac{\left(\frac{1}{5}\right)X}{X} \times 100$$

$$= \frac{1}{5} \times 100$$

= 20% {canceling the common factor 5}

Gain percent = 20%

©All rights reserved-Math-Knots LLC., VA-USA

128. B

(I) **Charles bought a bicycle for $425 and sold it for $459. Find the gain percent.**

(II) 12%

Solution:

Selling price of bicycle = $459

Cost Price of bicycle = $425

Gain percent = ?

Gain = Selling price - Cost price

$$\text{Gain\%} = \frac{\text{Gain}}{\text{Cost Price}} \times 100$$

The selling price and cost price are given, so calculate the gain using the formula:

Gain = Selling Price - Cost Price

= $459 - $425 = $34

$$\text{Gain\%} = \frac{\text{Gain}}{\text{Cost Price}} \times 100$$

$$= \frac{\$34}{\$425} \times 100$$

= 8% {canceling the common factors}

gain % = 8%

129. A

(I) 25 ÷ 200= 0.125

(II) 0.1

©All rights reserved-Math-Knots LLC., VA-USA

130. C

(I) **Find the cost price when selling price is $700 and loss is 20%**

(II) **$875**

Selling price = $700
Loss percent = 20 %
To find: Cost price = ?

$$\text{Cost price} = \frac{100 \times \text{Selling price}}{(100 - \text{Loss\%})}$$

Cost price can be calculated using the formula:

$$\text{Cost price} = \frac{100 \times \text{Selling price}}{(100 - \text{Loss\%})} = \frac{100 \times 700}{(100 - 20)}$$

$$= \frac{100 \times 700}{80} = \frac{70000}{80}$$

= 875 {canceling the common factors}

131. C

(I) **Express 13/16 as percent**

(II) **81.25%**

To convert a given fraction to percentage, multiply the fraction with 100.

$$\frac{13}{16} \times 100 = \frac{1300}{16}$$

$$= 81.25$$

$$\frac{13}{16} = 81.25\%$$

©All rights reserved-Math-Knots LLC., VA-USA

132. B

(I) **Express 0.32 as percent.**

(II) **320%**

To convert a given decimal to percentage, multiply the decimal with 100.

0.32 x 100 = 32 %

0.32 = 32%

133. A

(I) **Express 24% as decimal**

(II) **0.024**

To convert a given percentage to decimal, divide the percentage numeral by 100 and place the decimal point at the appropriate place.

$$24\ \% = \frac{24}{100}$$

$$= 0.24$$

{There are 2 zeros in the denominator, so place the decimal point after 2 places from the right}

24% = 0.24

©All rights reserved-Math-Knots LLC., VA-USA

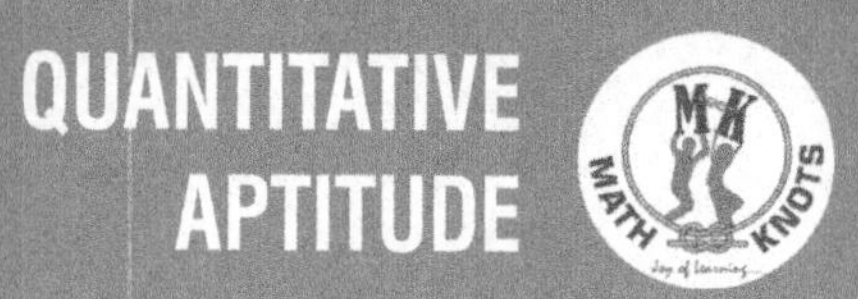

134. A

(I) **Find x, if 5% of x = 475**

(II) **950**

5 % of x = 475 = $\frac{5}{100}$.(x) = 475 {Expressing 5% as a fraction}

5x = 475 × 100 {By cross multiplication}

5x = 47500

x = $\frac{47500}{5}$ {dividing both sides by 5} = x = 9500

135. B

(I) **20 yards cloth is required to make 25 shirts. How much cloth is required to make 35 shirts of the same size?**

(II) **29**

Let the length of cloth required to make 35 shirts = y yards
More the number of shirts more the length of cloth required it is the case of direct variation.
ratio of number of shirts = ratio of length of cloth in yards
25: 35 :: 20 : y
20 x 35 = 25 x y {product of extremes = product of means}

25y = 20 x 35

y = $\frac{20 \times 35}{25}$ {Dividing both sides by 25}

y = 28 {Canceling the common factors}

Length of cloth required to make 35 shirts = 28 yards

©All rights reserved-Math-Knots LLC., VA-USA

136. C

(I) **If 8 ft long iron rod of uniform thickness weighs 28 lb, what will be the weight of 10 ft long iron rod of the same thickness**

(II) **35 lb**

Let the weight of 10 ft long iron rod of the same thickness = y lb
Longer the rod, heavier is the weight.
it is the case of direct variation.
ratio of length of rods = ratio of their weights
8 : 10 : : 28 : y
8y = 10 x 28 {product of extremes = product of means}

$y = \frac{10 \times 28}{8}$ {Dividing both sides by 8}

y = 35 {Canceling the common factors}
Weight of 10 ft long iron rod = 35 lb

137. C

(I) **Cube root of (- 3375 / 2197)**

(II) **15 / -13**

$\frac{\sqrt[3]{a}}{\sqrt[3]{b}} = \sqrt[3]{\frac{a}{b}}$; (-3375) = -(3 x 3 x 3 x 5 x 5 x 5)

$\sqrt[3]{-3375}$ - (3 x 5) = -15

2197 = 13 x 13 x 13

$\sqrt[3]{2917}$ = 13

$\sqrt[3]{\frac{-729}{4913}} = \frac{-15}{13}$

©All rights reserved-Math-Knots LLC., VA-USA

138. C

(I) The volume of a cubical box is 166.375 cubic inches. Find the length of each side of the box.

(II) 5.5 inches

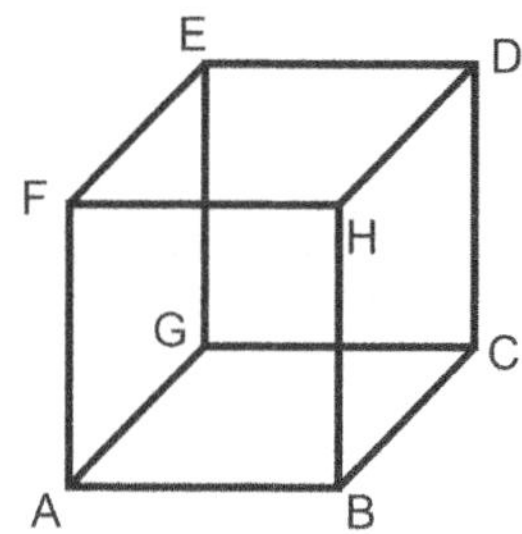

Let the length of side of cubical box = a

The volume of a cubical box = a^3

$= 166.375 \text{ inches}^3$

$a = \sqrt[3]{166.375}$

$\sqrt[3]{166.375} = \sqrt[3]{\frac{166375}{1000}}$

$= \frac{\sqrt[3]{166375}}{\sqrt[3]{1000}} \quad \{\frac{\sqrt[3]{a}}{\sqrt[3]{b}} = \sqrt[3]{\frac{a}{b}}\}$

Resolve 166375 as a product of prime factors and make triplets of similar factors. $166375 = \underline{5 \times 5 \times 5} \times \underline{11 \times 11 \times 11}$

$\sqrt[3]{166375} = 5 \times 11$

$= 55$

$1000 = \underline{10 \times 10 \times 10}$

$\sqrt[3]{1000} = 10$

$\sqrt[3]{166.375} = \frac{\sqrt[3]{166375}}{\sqrt[3]{1000}}$

$= \frac{55}{10}$

$= 5.5$

The length of side of cubical box = a = 5.5 inches

©All rights reserved-Math-Knots LLC., VA-USA

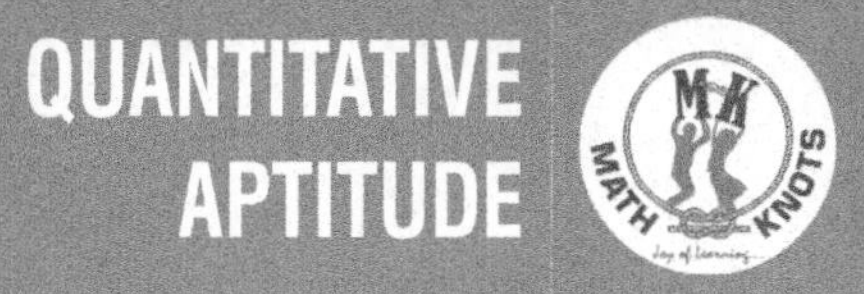

139. C

(I) **Find the cube root of 1331**

(II) 11

1331 as a product of prime factors and make triplets of similar factors.

$1331 = \underline{11 \times 11 \times 11}$

$\sqrt[3]{1331} = 11$

The cube root of 1331 is 11.

140. A

(I) **Find the smallest number with which 392 should be multiplied to make it a perfect cube.**

(II) 6

Write 392 as product of prime factors: $392 = \underline{2 \times 2 \times 2} \times 7 \times 7$

As factor 7 is a pair, not a triplet, clearly to make it a perfect cube, 392 must be multiplied by 7.

141. B

(I) $24^4 = 12^4 \text{ X } 2^4 = 12^4 \text{ X } 16$

(II) 12^6

142. A

(I) $20^3 = 20 \text{ X } 20 \text{ X } 20 = 8000$

(II) 2000

143. A

(I) $50^3 \text{ X } 20^3 = (50 \text{ X } 20)^3 = 1000^3 = 1{,}000{,}000{,}000$

(II) 10000

©All rights reserved-Math-Knots LLC., VA-USA

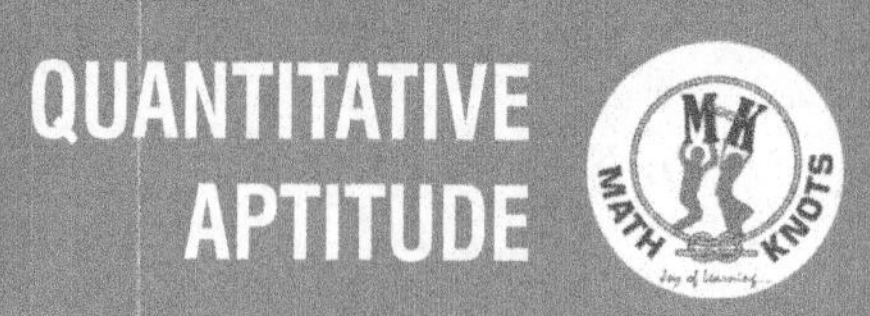

144. C

(I) **Find the smallest number by which 243 should be divided so that the quotient is a perfect cube**

(II) **9**

Write 243 as product of prime factors: $243 = \underline{3 \times 3 \times 3} \times 3 \times 3$
As the factor 3 appears 5 times (two more than a triplet),
Clearly to make it a perfect cube, 243 must be divided by 9

145. A

(I) $\sqrt{72} \times \sqrt{450}$

(II) **160**

$\sqrt{72} \times \sqrt{450} = \sqrt{32400}$ $\{ \sqrt{a} \times \sqrt{b} = \sqrt{ab} \}$

$\sqrt{32400} = \sqrt{180 \times 180} = 180$

146. C

(I) **806.5% = 806.5 / 100 = 8.065**

(II) **8.065**

147. C

(I) $\sqrt{\frac{63504}{65025}}$

(II) $\frac{84}{85}$

Solution: $\sqrt{\frac{63504}{65025}} = \frac{\sqrt{63504}}{\sqrt{65025}}$ $\{ \sqrt{\frac{a}{b}} = \frac{\sqrt{a}}{\sqrt{b}} \}$

$\sqrt{63504} = \sqrt{252 \times 252} = 252$ $\sqrt{65025} = \sqrt{255 \times 255} = 255$

$$\sqrt{\frac{63504}{65025}} = \frac{\sqrt{63504}}{\sqrt{65025}} = \frac{252}{255} = \frac{84}{85}$$

©All rights reserved-Math-Knots LLC., VA-USA

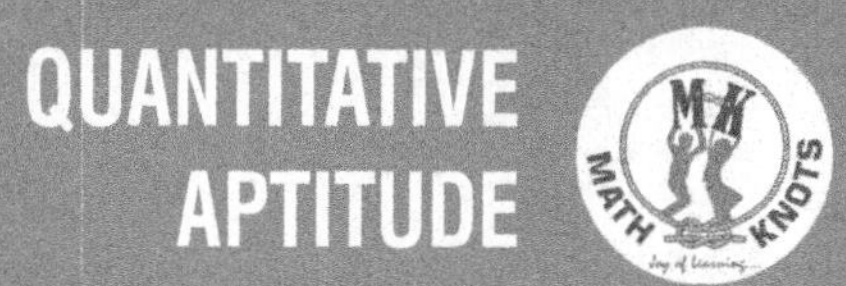

148. B

(I) $\sqrt{\left[\left(\frac{49}{225}\right) \times \left(\frac{625}{196}\right)\right]}$

(II) 25/6

Answer

$\sqrt{\left[\left(\frac{49}{225}\right) \times \left(\frac{625}{196}\right)\right]} \quad \frac{\sqrt{49} \times \sqrt{625}}{\sqrt{225} \times \sqrt{196}}$

$= \frac{7 \times 25}{15 \times 14}$

$= \frac{5}{6}$ {Canceling the common factors}

149. C

(I) Area of the circle / Perimeter of the semi-circle
= Radius / 2

(II) Radius / 2

150. B

(I) Area of the Square / Perimeter of the Square
= Side length of the Square / 4

(II) Side length of the Square / 2

©All rights reserved-Math-Knots LLC., VA-USA

151. A

(I) $\sqrt{(81/289)} \times \sqrt{(324/2916)}$

(II) 3 / 19

$\sqrt{(81/289)} \times \sqrt{(324/2916)} = \sqrt{\frac{81 \times 324}{289 \times 2916}}$

$= \sqrt{\frac{9}{289}}$ {Canceling the common factors}

$= \frac{\sqrt{9}}{\sqrt{289}}$ $\{\sqrt{\frac{a}{b}} = \frac{\sqrt{a}}{\sqrt{b}}\}$

$= \frac{3}{17}$

152. B

(I) $\sqrt{\frac{121}{169}}$

(II) 11/7

$\sqrt{\frac{121}{169}} = \frac{\sqrt{121}}{\sqrt{169}}$ $\{\sqrt{\frac{a}{b}} = \frac{\sqrt{a}}{\sqrt{b}}\}$

By prime factorization we get, 121 = 11 x 11

$\sqrt{121} = 11$

169 = 13 x 13

$\sqrt{169} = 13$

$\sqrt{\frac{121}{169}} = \frac{\sqrt{121}}{\sqrt{169}} = \frac{11}{13}$

©All rights reserved-Math-Knots LLC., VA-USA

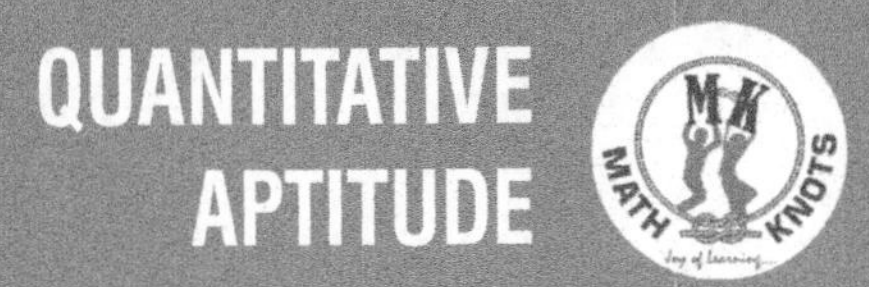

153. A

(I) **The surface area of a ball is 113.04 $inches^2$. Find the volume of the ball. (Given, Π = 3.14)**

(II) **113 $inches^3$**

Formula: The surface area of a sphere = $4\pi r^2$ square units
Volume of a sphere = $(4/3)\pi r^3$ cubic units

Surface area of a sphere = $4\pi r^2$ square units
$4\pi r^2 = 113.04\ inches^2$

$4 \times 3.14 \times r^2 = 113.04$

$r^2 = \frac{113.04}{4 \times 3.14}$

$r^2 = 9$
$r = \sqrt{9}$

r = 3 inches

Volume of a sphere = $(4/3)\pi r^3$ cubic units
$= (4/3) \times 3.14 \times 3 \times 3 \times 3$
$= 113.04\ inches^3$

Volume of a sphere = 113.04 $inches^3$

©All rights reserved-Math-Knots LLC., VA-USA

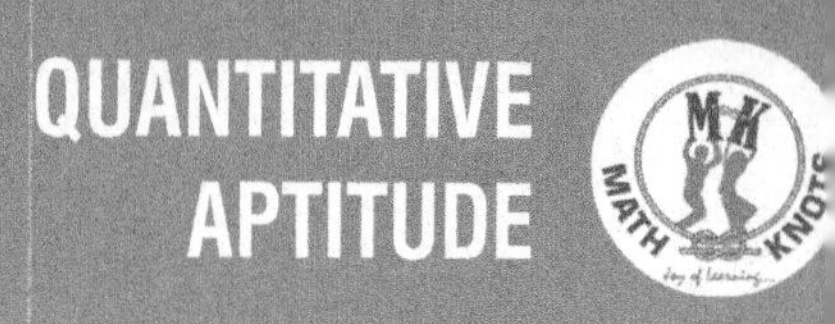

154. C

(I) **Find the volume of a sphere whose diameter is 24 inches. (Given, π = 3.14)**

(II) **7234.56 inches^3**

Diameter of the sphere (d) = 24 inches

Radius of the sphere (r) = 24/2

= 12 inches

Volume of the sphere = (4/3) π r^3

$$= \frac{4 \times 3.14 \times 12 \times 12 \times 12}{3}$$

= 7234.56 inches^3

The volume of the sphere = 7234.56 inches^3

155. C

(I) **The circumference of the base of a right circular cylinder is 62.8 inches and its height is 15 inches. Find the volume of the cylinder. (Given, π = 3.14)**

(II) **4710 inches^3**

Circumference of the base of a right circular cylinder = 62.8 inches

$2 \pi r = 62.8$

$6.28 \times r = 62.8$

$$r = \frac{62.8}{6.28}$$

r = 10 inches

Radius, r = 10 inches

Volume of cylinder = π $r^2 h$ = 3.14 x 10 x 10 x 15 = 4710 inches^3

©All rights reserved-Math-Knots LLC., VA-USA

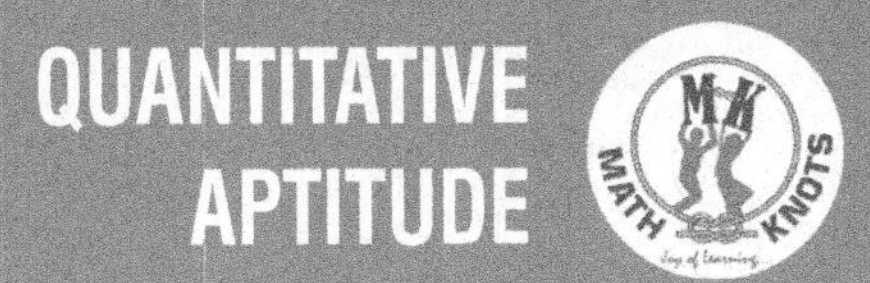

156. B

(I) $\sqrt{0.0625}$

(II) 0.5

0.0625 = 625 / 10000 = (25 X 25) / (100 X 100)

$\sqrt{0.0625}$ = 25 / 100 = 0.25

157. C

(I) $\sqrt{1089}$

(II) 33

A given number is a perfect square if it is expressible as the product of pairs of equal factors.

By prime factorization,

1089 = $\underline{3 \times 3} \times \underline{11 \times 11}$

$\sqrt{1089}$ = 3 x 11

= 33

158. A

(I) **Arithmetic mean of first twelve natural numbers.**

(II) 6.0

The first 12 natural numbers are:

1, 2, 3, 4, 5, 6, 7, 8, 9, 10,11and 12

Mean = $\dfrac{\text{Sum of the natural numbers}}{\text{Number of natural numbers}}$

$= \dfrac{1 + 2 + 3 + 4 + 5 + 6 + 7 + 8 + 9 + 10 + 11 + 12}{12}$

$= \dfrac{78}{12} = 6.5$

©All rights reserved-Math-Knots LLC., VA-USA

159. A

(I) **Mean of first fifteen even numbers.**

(II) **15**

The first 15 even numbers are:

2, 4, 6, 8, 10, 12, 14, 16, 18, 20, 22, 24, 26, 28 and 30

$$\text{Mean} = \frac{\text{Sum of the even numbers}}{\text{Number of even numbers}}$$

$$= \frac{2 + 4 + 6 + 8 + 10 + 12 + 14 + 16 + 18 + 20 + 22 + 24 + 26 + 28 + 30}{15}$$

$$= \frac{240}{15} = 16$$

160. A

(I) **Mean of first 10 prime numbers.**

(II) **12.5**

The first 10 prime numbers are:

2, 3, 5, 7, 11, 13, 17, 19, 23 and 29

$$\text{Mean} = \frac{\text{Sum of the prime numbers}}{\text{Number of prime numbers}}$$

$$= \frac{2 + 3 + 5 + 7 + 11 + 13 + 17 + 19 + 23 + 29}{10}$$

$$= \frac{129}{10}$$

$$= 12.9$$

©All rights reserved-Math-Knots LLC., VA-USA

161. A

(I) The marks obtained by 15 students are as follows: 53, 48, 68, 87, 67, 84, 29, 34, 91, 44, 45, 32, 65, 19, 35. If 35 is the pass mark, how many students have failed?

(II) 1

Arranging the given data in ascending order:
19, 29 32, 34, 35, 44, 45, 48, 53, 65, 67, 68, 84, 87, 91

S.NO	Marks Obtained	Frequency (Students)
1	19	1
2	29	1
3	32	1
4	34	1
5	35	1
6	44	1
7	45	1
8	48	1
9	53	1
10	65	1
11	67	1
12	68	1
13	84	1
14	87	1
15	91	1

©All rights reserved-Math-Knots LLC., VA-USA

162. B

(I) The points obtained by 10 students are as follows:
53, 48, 87, 67, 34, 91, 45, 32, 19, 35
How many students have scored more than 65 points?

(II) 5

Arranging the given data in ascending order:
19, 32, 34, 35, 45, 48, 53, 67, 87, 91

S.NO	Points Obtained	Frequency
1	19	1
2	32	1
3	34	1
4	35	1
5	45	1
6	48	1
7	53	1
8	67	1
9	87	1
10	91	1

From the above table,
Students scoring 67 points = 1
Students scoring 87 points = 1
Students scoring 91 points = 1
Students scoring more than 65 points = 1 + 1 + 1 = 3

©All rights reserved-Math-Knots LLC., VA-USA

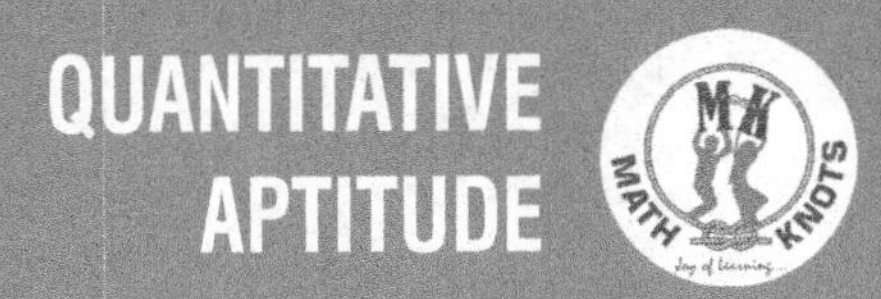

163. C

(I) A die was thrown 20 times and the following scores were obtained

1, 5, 3, 4, 2, 6, 2, 5, 3, 1

4, 2, 1, 4, 3, 2, 4, 6, 3, 4

What is the most frequent score

(II) 4

Arranging the given data in ascending order:

1, 1, 1, 2, 2, 2, 2, 3, 3, 3, 3, 4, 4, 4, 4, 4, 5, 5, 6, 6

S.NO	Scores on the die	Frequency
1	1	3
2	2	4
3	3	4
4	4	5
5	5	2
6	6	2

From the above table,

Score 4 occurs the highest number of times (5 times).

4 is the most frequent score

©All rights reserved-Math-Knots LLC., VA-USA

164. C

(I) $5 - \frac{2(x - 4)}{3} = \frac{(2x + 3)}{2}$

(II) $x = 3.7$

$5 - \frac{2(x - 4)}{3} = \frac{(2x + 3)}{2}$

LCM of the denominators 3 and 2 is 6.

$6(5) - 12\,\frac{(x - 4)}{3} = 6\,\frac{(2x + 3)}{2}$ {Multiplying both sides by 6}

$30 - 4\,(x - 4) = 3\,(2x + 3)$

$30 - 4x + 16 = 6x + 9$

$46 - 4x = 6x + 9$

$-4x - 6x = -46 + 9$ {To get like terms together, transpose 6x to LHS and 46 to RHS}

$-10x = -37$

$x = \frac{37}{10}$ {Dividing both sides by -10}

$x = 3.7$

©All rights reserved-Math-Knots LLC., VA-USA

165. B

(I) $(p + 1) / (p - 3) = 3/4$

(II) 13

$$\frac{p+1}{p-3} = \frac{3}{4}$$

$4(p + 1) = 3(p - 3)$

$4p + 4 = 3p - 9$

$4p - 3p = -9 - 4$ {To get like terms together transpose 3p to LHS and 4 to RHS}

$p = -13$

166. A

(I) $(x^2 + 4) / (3x^2 + 7) = \frac{1}{2}$ (where x is positive)

(II) 0.11

$$\frac{x^2+4}{3x^2+7} = \frac{1}{2}$$

$2(x^2 + 4) = 1(3x^2 + 7)$ {by cross multiplication}

$2x^2 + 8 = 3x^2 + 7$

$2x^2 - 3x^2 = -8 + 7$ {To get like terms together transpose $3x^2$ to LHS and 8 to RHS}

$-x^2 = -1$

$x^2 = 1$ {Canceling negative sign both sides}

$x = 1$ {Positive value}

©All rights reserved-Math-Knots LLC., VA-USA

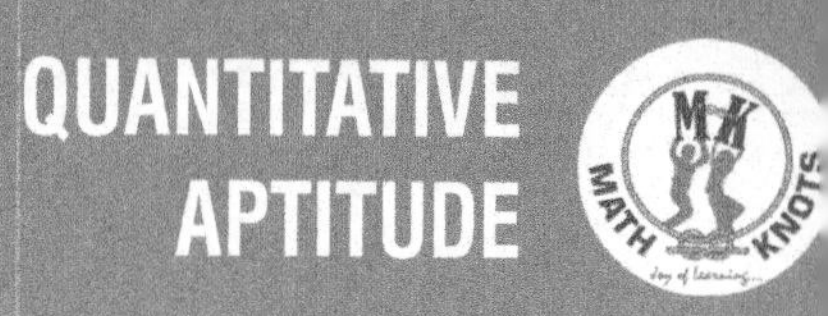

167. C

(I) $(x^2+5)\left(x^2-\frac{1}{5}\right)$

(II) $x^4+\frac{24x^2}{5}-1$

$(x + a)(x + b) = x^2 + (a + b)x + ab$

Solution:

Here a = 5

$b = \frac{-1}{8}$

Using the above identity,

$$(x^2+5)\left(x^2-\frac{1}{5}\right) = (x^2)^2+\left(5-\frac{1}{5}\right)x^2+5\left(\frac{-1}{5}\right)$$

$$= x^4+\frac{24x^2}{5}-1$$

$$(x^2+5)\left(x^2-\frac{1}{5}\right) = x^4+\frac{24x^2}{5}-1$$

168. B

(I) **4(x + 2) - x = 5x +11**

(II) **-2/3 Feet**

4 (x + 2) - x = 5x +11

4x + 8 - x = 5x + 11 {simplifying}

3x + 8 = 5x + 11 {simplifying}

3x - 5x = 11 - 8 {transposing 5x to LHS and 8 to RHS}

-2x = 3

$x = \frac{-3}{2}$ {dividing both sides by -2}

©All rights reserved-Math-Knots LLC., VA-USA

169. C

(I) **After 12 years Sam will be three times as old as he was 4 years ago. Find his present age.**

(II) **12**

Let the present age of Sam be x years.
His age 4 years ago = (x - 4) years
His age after 12 years = (x + 12) years
$(x + 12) = 3 (x - 4)$
$x + 12 = 3x - 12$
$12 + 12 = 3x - x = 24 = 2x$
$x = \frac{24}{2}$ {dividing both sides by 2}

$x = 12$

170. B

(I) **The sum of two consecutive odd numbers is 92. Find the least nuber.**

(II) **47**

Let the first odd number be (2x + 1)
Second consecutive odd number = (2x + 3)
According to question,
$(2x + 1) + (2x + 3) = 92$
$4x + 4 = 92$
$4x = 92 - 4 = 4x = 88$

$x = \frac{88}{4}$ {dividing both sides by 4}

$x = 22$
The required numbers are :
$(2x + 1) = (2 \times 22) + 1 = 45$
$(2x + 3) = (2 \times 22) + 3 = 47$
The 2 consecutive odd numbers are 45 and 47.

©All rights reserved-Math-Knots LLC., VA-USA

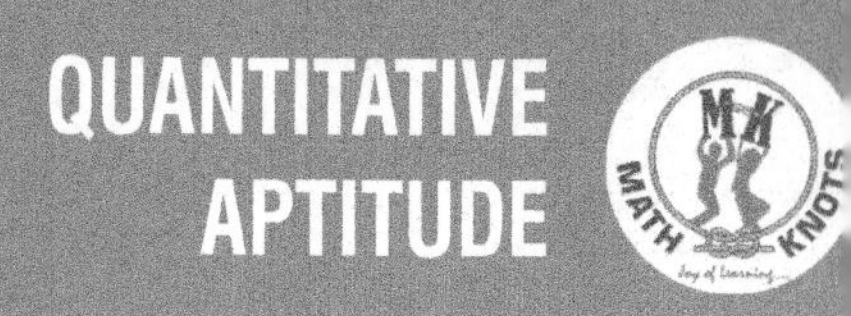

171. A

(I) **The sides of a triangle are in the ratio 3:5:4. If the perimeter of the triangle is 48 inches, find the measure of its greatest side.**

(II) **16**

Perimeter of a triangle = Sum of its 3 sides

Let the common factor of the given ratio be x.

The sides of the triangle are 3x, 5x and 4x inches.

Perimeter of the triangle = 48 inches

$3x + 5x + 4x = 48$

$12x = 48$

$x = \frac{48}{12}$ {dividing both sides by 12}

$x = 4$

The measures of sides of the triangle are:

$3x = 3 \times 4 = 12$ inches

$5x = 5 \times 4 = 20$ inches

$4x = 4 \times 4 = 16$ inches

The sides of the triangle measure 12 inches, 20 inches and 16 inches.

172 B.

(I) **The ratio of two numbers is 3:7 and their sum is 100. Find the least of two numbers.**

(II) **65**

Let the common factor of the given ratio be x.

The first number = 3x

The second number = 7x

$3x + 7x = 100$

$10x = 100 = x = 10$

The first number = $3x = 3 \times 10 = 30$

The second number = $7x = 7 \times 10 = 70$

The two numbers are 30 and 70.

©All rights reserved-Math-Knots LLC., VA-USA

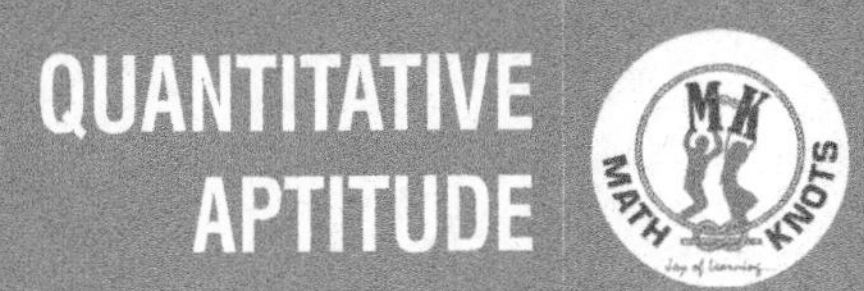

173. A

(I) A room 14 ft by 12 ft is to be paved with stones, each measuring 0.25 ft by 0.2 ft. Find the number of stones required to pave the room.

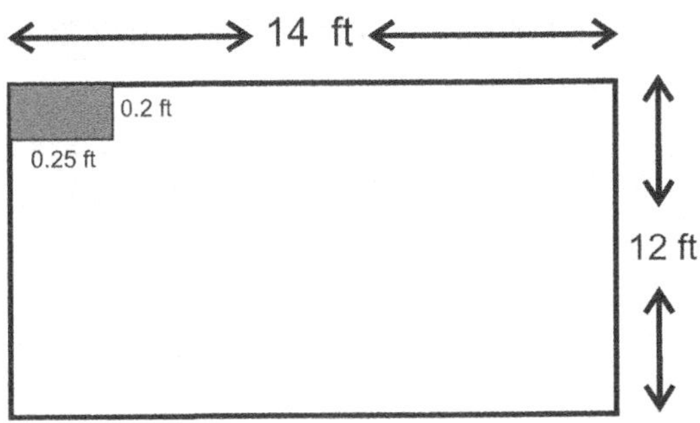

(II) 336

Area of room = L x W
= 14 ft x 12 ft
= 168 ft^2

Area of room = 168 ft^2

Area of a stone = l x w
= 0.25 ft x 0.2 ft
= 0.05 ft^2

Area of a stone = 0.05 ft^2

Number of stones required for paving = $\frac{\text{Area of the room}}{\text{Area of a stone}}$

$= \frac{168}{0.05}$

= 3,360

©All rights reserved-Math-Knots LLC., VA-USA

174. C

(I) Find the product of $2x$ and $(3x - 4y^2)$

(II) $6x^2 - 8xy^2$

Multiply each term of the first polynomial with each term of the second polynomial and add the products.

$(2x) . (3x - 4y^2) = (2x) . (3x) + (2x) . (-4y^2)$

$= (2 . 3)\ x^{1+1} + (2 . -4)\ xy^2 \{a^m \times a^n = a^{m+n}\}$

$= 6x^2 - 8xy^2$

175. B

(I) $(2x + 5y)(2x - 5y)$

(II) $4x^2 + 25y^2$

$(a + b)(a - b) = (a^2 - b^2)$

$(2x + 5y)(2x - 5y) = (2x)^2 - (5y)^2$

$= (2x)(2x) - (5y)(5y)$

$= 4x^2 - 25y^2$

176. C

(I) Area of a Semi Circle X 1/2

= ∏ X Length of radius X Length of radius X 1/2 X 1/2

(II) ∏ X Length of radius X Length of radius X 1/4

177. A

(I) $27^8 = (3 \times 3 \times 3)^8 = 3^{24}$

(II) 3^{16}

©All rights reserved-Math-Knots LLC., VA-USA

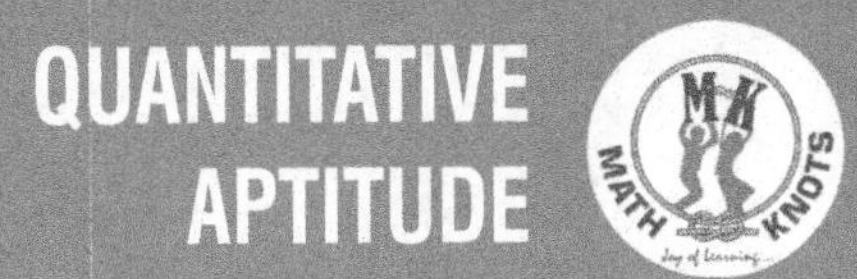

178. C

(I) Expand the following: $\left(2a + \frac{b}{7}\right)^2$

(II) $4a^2 + \frac{4ab}{7} + \frac{b^2}{49}$

$$(x+y)^2 = x^2 + 2xy + y^2$$

$$\left(2a + \frac{b}{7}\right)^2 = (2a)^2 + \left(2 \times (2a) \times \frac{b}{7}\right) + \left(\frac{b}{7}\right)^2$$

$$= (2a)(2a) + \left(2 \times (2a) \times \frac{b}{7}\right) + \left(\frac{b}{7}\right)\left(\frac{b}{7}\right)$$

$$= 4a^2 + \frac{4ab}{7} + \frac{b^2}{49}$$

179. C

(I) $25^3 \text{ X } 49^3 = (5\times5)^3 \times (7\times7)^3 = 5^6 \times 7^6 = 35^6$

(II) 35^6

180. B

(I) $(11 - 19b^2 - b) + (b^2 - 3b^3 + b) + (3b^2 + 21)$

(II) $32 - 15b^2$

$(11 - 19b^2 - b) + (b^2 - 3b^3 + b) + (3b^2 + 21)$

$= 11 - 19b^2 - b + b^2 - 3b^3 + b + 3b^2 + 21$

$= (11 + 21) + (- b + b) + (- 19b^2 + b^2 + 3b^2) - 3b^3$

$= 32 + (-1 + 1)\, b + (-19 + 1 + 3)\, b^2 - 3b^3$

$= 32 + (0)\, b + (-15)\, b^2 - 3b^3$

$= 32 - 15b^2 - 3b^3$

©All rights reserved-Math-Knots LLC., VA-USA

181. A

(I) **Pamela saves 15% of her income. If her monthly saving is $600, what is her monthly income?**

(II) 3600

Let the monthly income of Pamela = $y

Pamela saves 15% of her income.

Or, Pamela saves 15% of $y

15% of $y = $600

$\frac{15}{100} \times y = 600$ {Expressing 15% as a fraction}

$15y = 600 \times 100$ {By cross multiplication}

$15y = 60000$

$y = \frac{60000}{15}$ {Dividing both sides by 15}

$y = 4,000$ {Canceling the common factors}

©All rights reserved-Math-Knots LLC., VA-USA

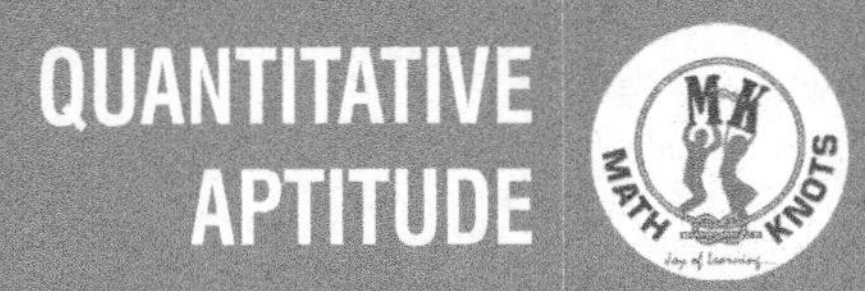

182. C

(I) Find the ratio of 35 cm to 15 m. (Given, 1 m = 100 cm)

(II) 7:300

To express as ratio, the units of the two quantities should be same. So, we convert 15 m to its corresponding cm.

15 m = 15 × 100 cm {1 m = 100 cm}
= 1500 cm
The ratio of 35 cm to 15 m = 35:1500

$= \frac{35}{1500}$

$= \frac{7}{300}$ {Dividing by HCF of 35 and 1500 i.e. 5}

= 7:300

183. A

(I) $10^3 + (10^3 - 10^2) + (10^2 - 10) + (10 - 8)$
$10^3 + 10^3 - 8 = 2000 - 8 = 1992$
or 1000 + 900 + 90 + 2 = 1992

(II) 1991

184. C

(I) In a leap year 72nd day of the year
January has 31 days
February has 29 days
March ,12th is 72nd day

(II) March 12th

©All rights reserved-Math-Knots LLC., VA-USA

185. A
(I) Average of nine 9's is 9
(II) 8

186. B
(I) Sum of the Prime numbers between 1 and 10
2 + 3 + 5 + 7 = 17
(II) 19

187. A
(I) Length of the side of a square is what percent of its perimeter?
(II) 20%

Solution:
Length of Side =a units
(a / 4a) X 100 = 1/4 % = 0.25 %

188. A
(I) Number of edges of the cube
(II) 8

Solution: Top 4 edges, bottom has 4 edges and sides have 4 edges
Total : 4 + 4 + 4 = 12

189. B
(I) Twice the number plus 4 is 18.
(II) Number = 9

2X + 4 = 18 ---> 2X = 14 ---> X = 7

©All rights reserved-Math-Knots LLC., VA-USA

190. B

(I) The ratio of the side of a square to its perimeter
Length of the side / (4 X Length of the side)
= 1 / 4 = 1 : 4

(II) 4:1

191. C

(I) Fifty-five ,55's = 55 X 55

(II) 11 X 11 X 25 = 11 X 11 X 5 X 5 = 55 X 55

192. A

(I) A bird eats one worm every 5 minutes for an hour.

(II) 10

Solution:
60 Minutes make an hour.
60 / 5 = 12 .
12 groups of 5 minutes in an hour.
Bird eats 12 worms in total

193. B

(I) Sum of two largest primes less than 30
29 + 23 = 52

(II) 53

194. C

(I) 200 % of 50 %

(II) 100 %

©All rights reserved-Math-Knots LLC., VA-USA

195. C

(I) $2019201920192019 \div 2019$

(II) 1000100010001

196. C

(I) $5x = 10y$

(II) $8y = 4x$

197. B

(I) $3^{99} + 3^{99} + 3^{99} = 3^{99}(1 + 1 + 1) = 3^{99} \times 3 = 3^{100}$

(II) 3^{297}

198. A

(I) 2∏

(II) Length of radius = Side length of Square.
Area of a Circle / Area of a Square

Area of a Circle / Area of a Square
= (∏ X Length of radius X Length of radius) / (Length of radius X Length of radius) = ∏

199. A

(I) $33 \times 10 + 33 \times 10^2 + 33 \times 10^3$
$= 33 \times (10 + 100 + 1000) = 33 \times 1110$

(II) 33×1110

©All rights reserved-Math-Knots LLC., VA-USA

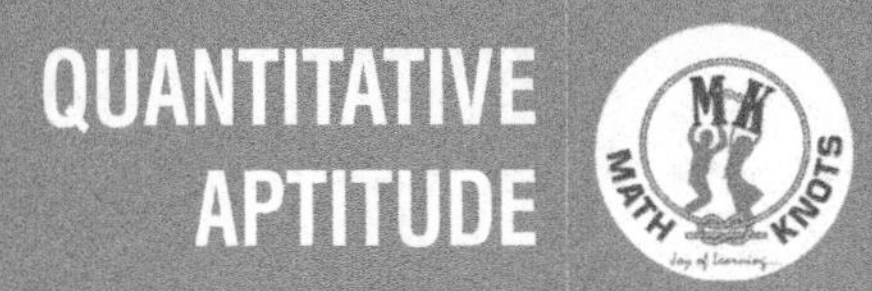

200. A

(I) 600 % of One hour

600 % of One hour = (600 / 24) % = 25% of One day

(II) 24 % of One day

201. B

(I) 1999 Quarters

1 Quarter = 5 Nickel's

1999 X 5 Nickel's

(II) 1999 X 10 Nickel's

202. A

(I) May has how many more seconds than April

(II) 24 X 360 Seconds

Solution:

April has 30 days , May has 31 days. May has one more day

One day = 24 hours and each hour has 60 Minutes and each minute has 60 seconds

One day = 24 X 60 X 60 = 24 X 3600 Seconds

203. B

(I) Average Arithmetic Mean of 2^4, 2^6, 2^8 and 2^{10}

(II) 2^8

Solution:

$2^8 = 2^2 \times 2 \times 2 \times 2 \times 2 \times 2 \times 2 = 2^2 \times 64$

$(2^4 + 2^6 + 2^8 + 2^{10}) / 4 = 2^4 (1 + 4 + 16 + 64) / 2^2$

$= 2^2(85)$

©All rights reserved-Math-Knots LLC., VA-USA

204. C

(I) The product of all the integers from -25 to +25 inclusive

(II) The sum of all the integers from -25 to 25 inclusive

Solution:

(-25) (-24) .....(-1) (0) (1) ....(24) (25) = 0

(Dont forget Zero is an integer and zero multiplied by any number gives a value of Zero)

(-25) + (-24) .....(-1) + (0) + (1) ....(24) + (25) = 0

(Each negative integer adding to corresponding positive integer becomes Zero)

205. C

(I) $(1-\frac{1}{2}) \times (1-\frac{1}{3}) \times (1-\frac{1}{4}) \times (1-\frac{1}{5}) \times (1-\frac{1}{6}) = \frac{1}{6}$

(II) $\frac{1}{6}$

206. D

(I) ab = 1 ; a + b

(II) 2

Solution:

a = 1 , b= 1 ; a . b = 1 ----> a + b = 2

a= 2 , b = 1/2 ; a . b = 1 ----> a + b = 2 + 1/2 = 5/2

Cannot be determined

207. B

(I) 2 Quaks = 3 Racks and 2 Racks = 3 Darks then 9 Darks = ?

(II) 5 Quaks

Solution :

4 Quacks = 6 Racks and 6 Racks = 9 Darks

©All rights reserved-Math-Knots LLC., VA-USA

208. B

(I) Car A can go 5 miles in 7 hours; Car A's average speed

(II) Car B can go 3 miles in 4 hours; Car B's average speed

Average speed = Distance traveled /Tame taken

Car A , average speed = 5/7

Car B , average speed = 3/4

I < II

209. C

(I) 80 % of 90 % of Y

(II) 72 % of Y

Solution:

80 % of 90 % of Y = (80 / 100) (90 / 100) Y= (72 / 100)
Y = 72 % Y

210. D

(I) a > b > c ; ab

(II) a > b > c ; ac

Answer:

a = 3 , b = 2 , c = 1 ; ab = 6 and ac = 3 ---> I > II
a = -1 , b = -2 , c = -3 ; ab = 2 and ac =6. ---> I < II

Cannot be determined

211. D

(I) $p > 0 ; p (p^2) (p^3)$

(II) $p > 0 ; p + p^2 + p^3$

I) $p = 1 ; p (p^2) (p^3) = 1 . 1 . 1 = 1$

II) $p = 1 ; p + p^2 + p^3 = 1 + 1 + 1 = 3$

I) $p = 2 ; p (p^2) (p^3) = 2 . 4 . 8 = 64$

II) $p = 2 ; p + p^2 + p^3 = 2 + 4 + 8 = 14$

Cannot be determined

©All rights reserved-Math-Knots LLC., VA-USA

212. C

(I) $1^3 + 1^5 + 1^1 = 1 + 1 + 1 = 3$

(II) $(-1)^2 + (-1)^4 + (-1)^6 = 1 + 1 + 1 = 3$

213. C

(I) The time to travel x miles at a speed of y miles per hour ; Time = x / y

(II) The time to travel 1/y miles at a speed of 1/x miles per hour = (1/y) / (1/x) = x/y

(Speed = Distance travelled / Time taken)

214. D

(I) (5 - x) (5 - x) (5 - x)

(II) (x - 5) (x - 5) (x - 5)

Solution:

I > II

(5 - x) (5 - x) (5 - x)

(x - 5) (x - 5) (x - 5) = - (5 - x) (5 - x) (5 - x)

or I < II

(5 - x) (5 - x) (5 - x) = - (x - 5) (x - 5) (x - 5)

(x - 5) (x - 5) (x - 5)

Can't be determined

215. B

(I) (-1)(-2) / (-3)

(II) (-1 -2) / -3

Solution:

I) (-1)(-2) / (-3) = -2/3

II) (-1 -2) / -3 = -3 /-3 = 1

©All rights reserved-Math-Knots LLC., VA-USA

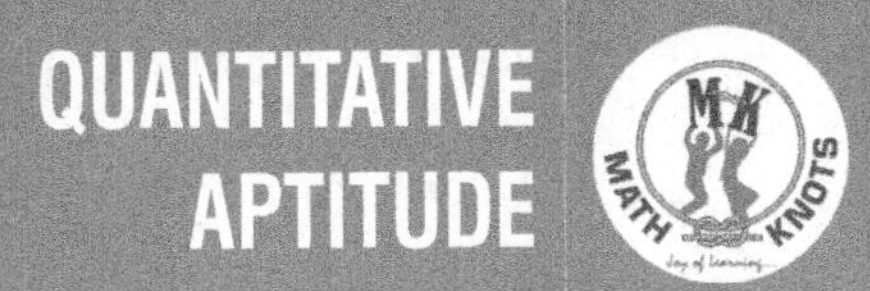

216. D

a and b are positive integers; $a^b = 64$

(I) a

(II) b

ab = 64 ; ab = 64 = 43 = 26

I >II ; 43 here a = 4 and b = 3

or I <II ; 2^6 here a = 2 and b = 6

Cannot be determined

217. B

(I) The 12th decimal digit of the fraction 1/8 as a decimal

(II) 5

Solution:

1/8 =0.125000000000

12th decimal digit is zero

I < II

218. C

(I) Ratio of 93 Seconds to 93 Hours

(II) Ratio of 193 Seconds to 193 Hours

93 Seconds / 93 Hours = 93 / 93 (60) (60) = 1 / (60) (60)

193 Seconds / 193 Hours = 193 / 193 (60) (60) = 1 / (60) (60)

219. B

(I) $\sqrt{4} + \sqrt{400} = 2 + 20 = 22$

(II) $\sqrt{40} + \sqrt{4000} = 2\sqrt{10} + 20\sqrt{10} = 22\sqrt{10}$

I < II

©All rights reserved-Math-Knots LLC., VA-USA

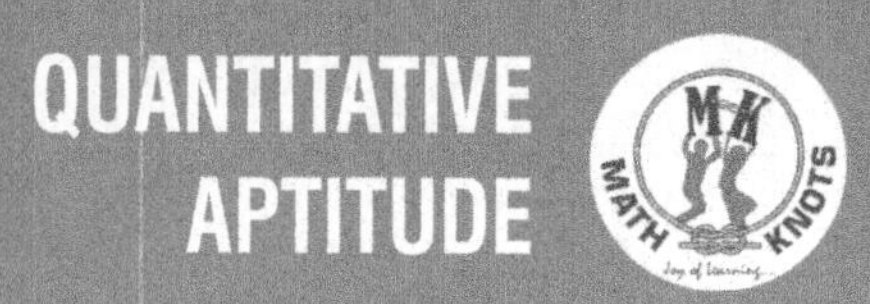

220. C

(I) $\sqrt{(41^2 - 40^2) / (5^2 - 4^2)} = \sqrt{9} = 3$

(II) 3

221. C

(I) 5 % of 18 % of 2 = (5/100) (18/100)(2)
= 180 / 10000

(II) 2 % of 30 % of 3 = (2/100) (30/100) (3)
= 180 / 10000

222. A

(I) The Area of a square with perimeter 1 = (1/4) (1/4) = 1/16 = 0.0625

(II) The Area of an equilateral triangle with perimeter 1
$(s)(s)(\sqrt{3})/4$

$(1/3)(1/3)(\sqrt{3})/4$
$= \sqrt{3}/36 = 0.048111$

223. C

(I) 17 (21 - 7) = 17 X 14

(II) 7 (10 + 4) + 10 (4 + 10)
= 7 X 14 + 10 X 14
= (7 + 10) X 14
= 17 X 14

224. C

(I) 2 Minute = 2 X 60 Seconds = 120 Seconds

(II) 120 Seconds

©All rights reserved-Math-Knots LLC., VA-USA

225. B

(I) $(\frac{1}{4})^5$ = 1/(4.4.4.4.4) = 1/1024

(II) $(\frac{1}{2})(\frac{1}{3})(\frac{1}{4})(\frac{1}{5})(\frac{1}{6})$ = 1/ (2.3.4.5.6) = 1/720

I < II

226. B

(I) The Average speed of a car going 2 miles in 5 hours.
= 2/5 mph

(II) The Average speed of a car going 1/2 mile in 1/5 hour.
= (1/2) / (1/5) = 5/2 mph

I < II

227. A

(I) The Number of edges a cube has = 12

(II) The Number of vertices a cube has = 8

228. A

(I) The average of the positive even integers from 2 to 20 inclusive.

Average = 11

(II) The average of the positive odd integers from 1 to 19 inclusive.

Average = 10

The Average of a group of equally spaced numbers is always in the middle of the group.

©All rights reserved-Math-Knots LLC., VA-USA

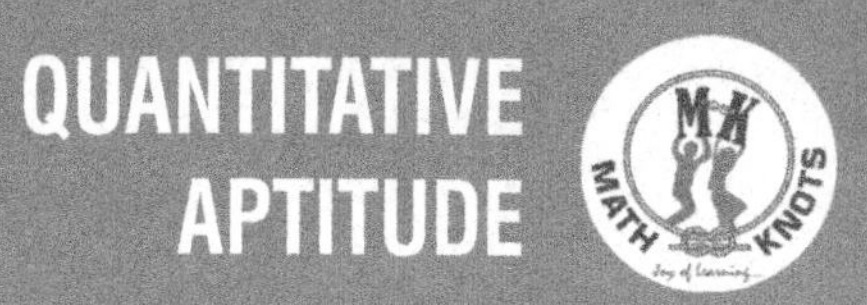

229. D

(I) The distance traveled at a speed of 50 miles per hour

(II) The distance traveled at a speed of 30 miles per hour

Since time taken is not provided. Distance cannot be determined
Cannot be determined.

230. A

(I) The smallest four-digit number without repeated digits is subtracted from the largest four digit number without repeated digits, the result is ?
9876 - 1234 = 8642

(II) 8640

231. A

(I) Area of an equilateral triangle with side $\sqrt{3} = \frac{3\sqrt{3}}{4}$

(II) $\sqrt{3} / 4$

232. C

(I) Radius of the Circle = Area of the Circle
Length of radius = ∏ X Length of radius X Length of radius
1 = Length of radius X ∏
Length of radius = 1 / ∏

(II) Length of radius = 1 / ∏

©All rights reserved-Math-Knots LLC., VA-USA

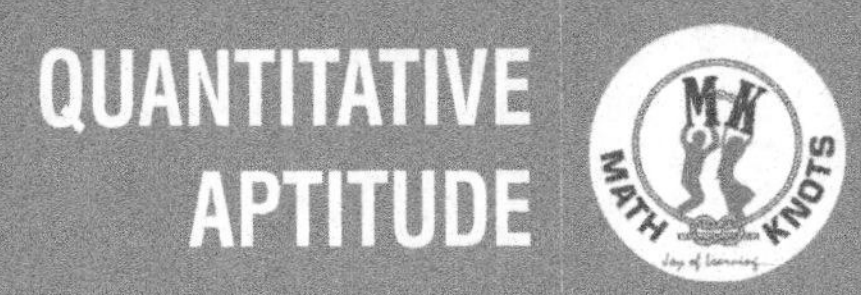

233. A
(I) How many numbers are in the range of 100 and 400 inclusive contains the digit 3 ?
(II) 136

Solution: 130-139 --> 11 numbers
230-239 --> 11 numbers
300-399 --> 120 numbers

103,113,123,143,153,163,173,183,193,203,213,223,243
253,263,273,283,293 ---> 18 numbers
Total: 120 + 11 + 11 + 18 = 160

234. B
(I) What is the 100th digit of the repeating decimal 0. 12367367367367....? (100th digit is 6)
(II) 7

235. C
(I) a % of b = ab / 100
(II) ab/100

236. B
(I) $(1000^2) / (252^2 - 248^2)$
(II) 1000

237. B
(I) Circumference of a circle is $2\pi r$
(II) 2 X Area of the circle is $2\pi r^2$

238. C
(I) 6 dozen pencils cost \$8.64
1 dozen pencils cost = \$8.64 / 6 = \$ 1.44
(II) A dozen pencils cost \$1.44

©All rights reserved-Math-Knots LLC., VA-USA

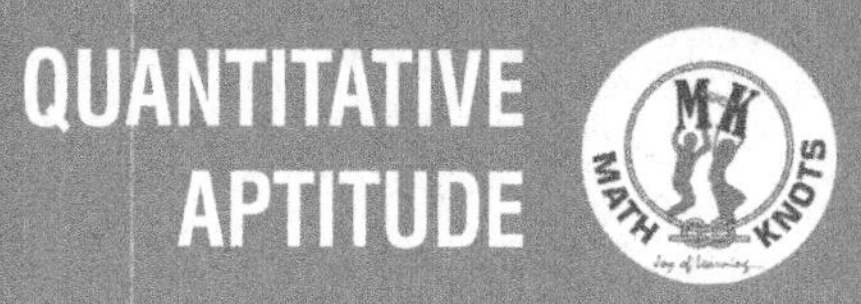

239. C

(I) A bag of chips cost \$0.35

(II) 16 bags of chips cost \$5.60

1 bag of chips = \$ 5.60 /16 = \$0.35

240. C

(I) A school has 500 students and 50 teachers. The ratio between the number of teachers and the number of students of the school.

(II) 1:10

Solution : $\frac{50}{500} = \frac{1}{10} = 1:10$

241. C

(I) Volume in cubic inches of the container shown in the figure below .

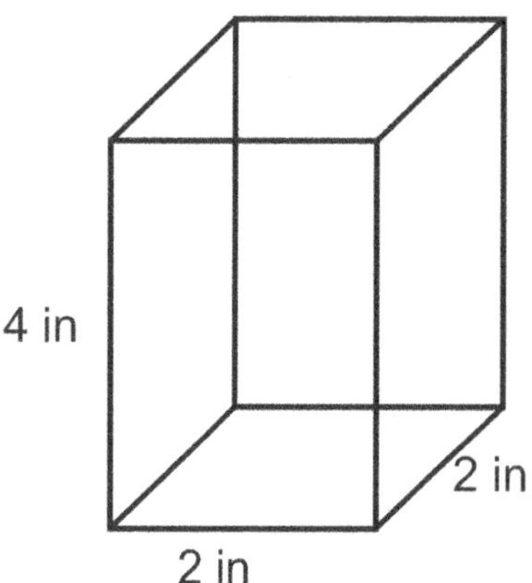

Solution: 4 X 2 X 2 = 16 Cubic Inches

(II) 16 Cubic Inches

©All rights reserved-Math-Knots LLC., VA-USA

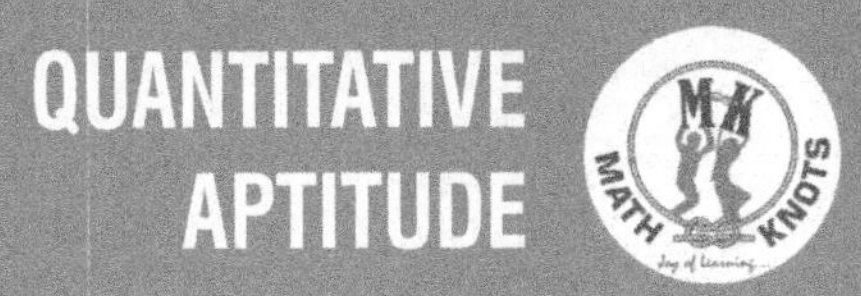

242. C

(I) Area in square centimeters of the right triangle in the figure below?

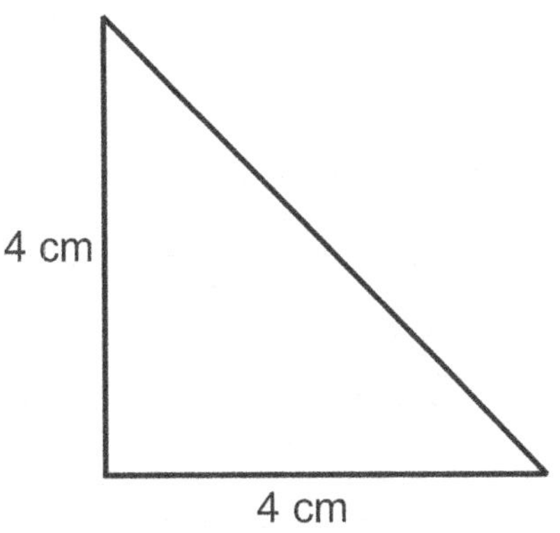

Solution: Area = (4 X 4)/ 2 = 8 sq.cm

(II) 8 sq.cm

243. B

(I) What percentage of the area of the triangle below is shadowed ? All triangles are equilateral.

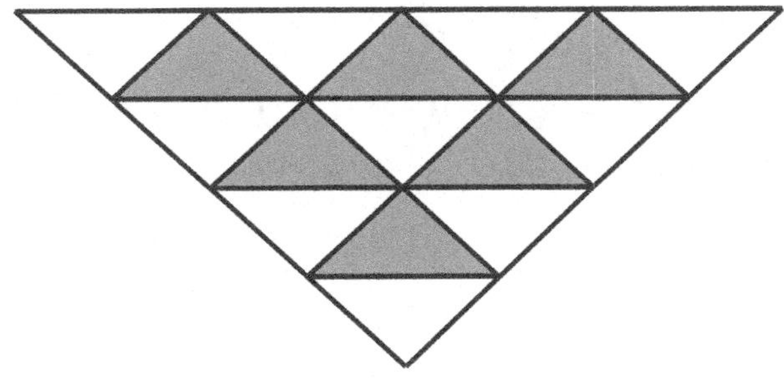

Solution: 6/16 = 0.375 or 37.5 %

(II) 62.5%

©All rights reserved-Math-Knots LLC., VA-USA

244. C

(I) $(5 + 3)^2 + (5 - 3)^2 = 64 + 4 = 68$

(II) 50 + 18

245. B

(I) Two sides of the right-angled triangle are 4 and 5. What is the length of the third side ?
3, 4, 5 are Pythagorean numbers. Third side is 3 units

(II) 7 + 2

246. C

(I) Two sides of the right-angled triangle are 7 and 24. What is the length of the third side ?
7, 24, 25 are Pythagorean numbers.Third side is 25 units

(II) 5 X 5

247. C

(I) What is the slope of the line that passes through the points P(-1,-4) and Q(3,5) ?
Solution: Slope = (5 -(-4)) / (3 - (-1))
= (5 + 4) / (3 + 1) = 9/4

(II) 9/4

248. C

(I) If T = U + 7 and U= 11 What is the value of T/4 ?
Solution:
T = U + 7 = 11 + 7 = 18 ; T/4 = 18/4 = 4.5

(II) 4.5

©All rights reserved-Math-Knots LLC., VA-USA

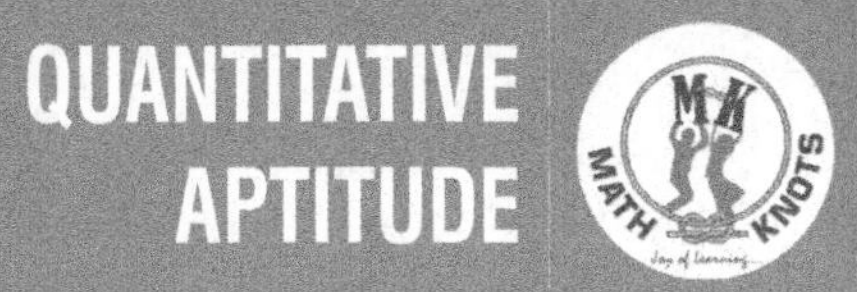

249. C

(I) Slope of the line

Y = (-6/5)X + 2/7 ?

Solution: Compare the given equation to

y = mx + c where m is slope

Slope = -6/5

(II) - 6/5

250. A

(I) Y-intercept of U = 3T+17 ?

Solution: Compare the given equation to

y = mx + c where c is y-intercept

So, y-intercept = 17

(II) 17 / 3

251. A

(I) Distance between numbers (-8) and 10

Solution: Distance = 10 - (-8) = 10 + 8 = 18

(II) 2

252. C

(I) Length of the rectangle is 10% more than width.

If the width of the rectangle is 10 cm

What is the area of the rectangle ?

Solution:

10 % of 10 = 1 ; Length is 10 + 1 = 11 cm

Area = 11 X 10 = 110 Sq.cm

(II) 110 Sq cm

©All rights reserved-Math-Knots LLC., VA-USA

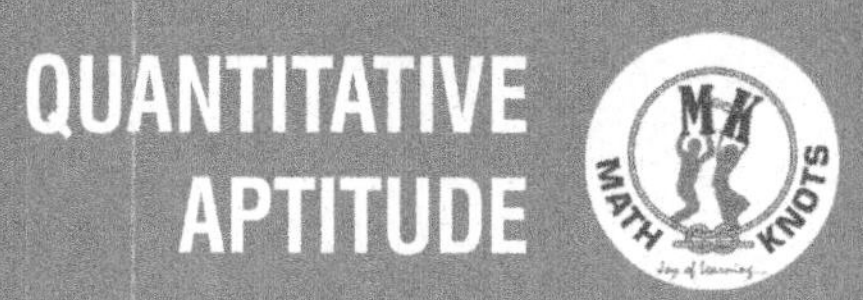

253. C

(I) A cat has 2 cats and each cat then has 4 cats each. How many legs are there all together ?
1 cat + 2 cats + 2 X 4 cats = 11 cats
each cat has 4 legs
Total legs are 11 X 4 = 44 legs

(II) 44 legs

254. A

(I) Sam wants to put tiles in her study room. She uses in total of 3750 tiles. There are 75 tiles in each row. How many such rows are there in the study room ?
Solution : 3750 / 75 = 50

(II) 10

255. B

(I) Zip Zing company is selling their hand bags for $175 which were originally priced as $250. What is percentage of discount offered ?
Solution: 175 / 250 = 0.70 or 70 % of original price
Discount = 100 % -70 % = 30 %

(II) 35%

256. C

(I) 10 Decades = 10 X 10 Years = 100 Years
(1 Decade = 10 Years)

(II) 100 Years

©All rights reserved-Math-Knots LLC., VA-USA

257. A

(I) 1 Decade = 10 Years = 10 X 365 Days

(II) 364 x 10 Days

258. A

(I) Two dice are rolled. The probability that the sum is greater than 3 ?

(II) 11 / 22

Solution:

Possible outcomes are :The sum of two dice:

	1	2	3	4	5	6
1	2	3	4	5	6	7
2	3	4	5	6	7	8
3	4	5	6	7	8	9
4	5	6	7	8	9	10
5	6	7	8	9	10	11
6	7	8	9	10	11	12

Answer: 33/36 = 11 / 12

259. C

(I) If the length of the Square K is doubled. Then its area increases by ?

Solution :

Length of square K = a units

Length of square K is doubled = 2 a

Area of square = (2a)(2a) = 4 (a X a)

(II) 4 times

©All rights reserved-Math-Knots LLC., VA-USA

260. C

(I) 10 donuts cost $11 There is a 5 % sales tax on the bill. Total bill is ?

Solution: 5 % of 11 = 5 X 11 / 100 = 55 / 100 = 0.55

Sales Tax = 0.55

Total bill = $11 + $0.55 = $11.55

(II) $11.55

261. C

(I) Rik solves 1 problem for every 8 sec. How many problems will he solve in 4 minutes ?

Solution:

4 minutes = 4 X 60 = 240 seconds = 8 X 30 seconds

30 problems can be solved in 4 minutes

(II) 30

262. C

(I) 175 % = 175 / 100 = 1.75

(II) 1.75

263. A

(I) 66 + 40 = 106

(II) 99 - 19 = 80

264. C

(I) A number is divisible by 1 and 29 only.

What is the number ?

Solution: 29

(II) 29

©All rights reserved-Math-Knots LLC., VA-USA

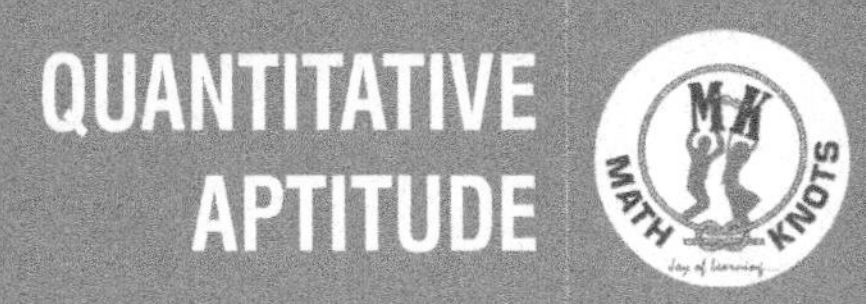

265. C

(I) $990 \div 10000 = 99 / 1000$

(II) $0.099 = 99 / 1000$

266. C

(I) 1,000,000

(II) $100^3 = 100 \times 100 \times 100 = 1{,}000{,}000$

267. C

(I) Greatest Common Factor of 63 and 42 ?
Greatest Common factor of 63 and 42 is 21

(II) 21

268. C

(I) Area of a Semi Circle

(II) $\pi \times$ Length of radius $\times$ Length of radius $\times \frac{1}{2}$

269. D

(I) Number of sides of Polygon

(II) Number of sides of Decagon

Solution: Polygon can have any number of sides.
Can't be determined

270. C

(I) 303

(II) Sum of the first 3 three-digit natural numbers
$= 100 + 101 + 102 = 303$

©All rights reserved-Math-Knots LLC., VA-USA

©All rights reserved-Math-Knots LLC., VA-USA

Made in the USA
Las Vegas, NV
29 May 2022